IRIS OF CHINA

中國的鳶尾

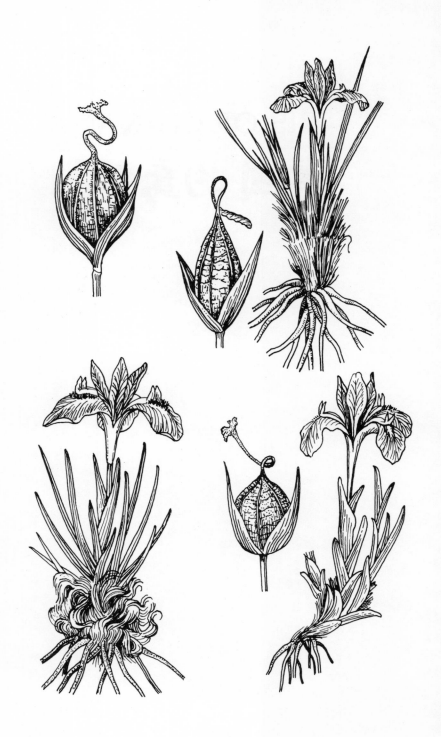

IRIS OF CHINA

*Chinese Iris in the Wild
and in the Garden*
by
James W. Waddick

The Iris of China
by
Zhao Yu-tang
translated by Youngjune Chang

TIMBER PRESS
Portland, Oregon

Frontispiece: *Iris potaninii* Maxim., *I. tigridia* Bunge, *I. kemaonensis* D. Don ex Royle (see Plate T). Drawn by Yu Zhen-zhou and Zhao Yu-tang.

ISBN 0-88192-207-2
Printed in Hong Kong

Part II of this book, The Iris of China by Zhao Yu-tang, was originally published in Chinese as Volume 16, Part I, of *Flora Reipublicae Popularis Sinicae*. Beijing: Science Press, 1985.

TIMBER PRESS, INC.
9999 S.W. Wilshire, Suite 124
Portland, Oregon 97225

Library of Congress Cataloging-in-Publication Data

Iris of China.
        p.   cm.
    "Part II of this book, The Iris of China ... was originally
published in Chinese as volume 16, part I of Flora reipublicae
popularis sinicae"--T.p. verso.
    Includes bibliographical references and index.
    Contents: Chinese iris in the wild and in the garden / by James W.
Waddick -- The iris of China / by Zhao Yu-tang ; translated by
Youngjune Chang.
    ISBN 0-88192-207-2
    1. Iris (Plant)--China.   I. Waddick, James W. Chinese iris in
the wild and in the garden. 1992. II. Chao, Yü-t'ang. Chung-kuo
chih wu chih. Ti 16 chüan, ti 1 fen ts'e. Pei tzu chih wu men, tan
tzu yeh chih wu kang. Yüan wei k'o. Yüan wei shu. English. 1992.
SB413.I8I845   1992
635.9'3424--dc20   91-19496
                                                              CIP

Contents

Color photographs follow page 16

Dedication

This book is for my favorite irisarians,
James L. Murrain and Caitlin J. Waddick,
as well as for all those people
who gave their support to this project.

James W. Waddick

Preface

This book is the result of the China Iris Project. The China Iris Project began as an informal discussion among three iris growers about the rarity of Chinese irises in cultivation. Sitting around the dining table of Bob Pries in St. Louis, Missouri, Jim Murrain, Bob, and I discussed the absence of many Chinese species from cultivation even though China is the home of more species of native iris than any other country in the world. Only a few species were known from several older collections. Naively we all assumed that it would be easy to fill these garden gaps by organizing a new collection trip for wild irises in China. These vague wishes grew into an independent effort to collect native *Iris* species in China, and I was deemed most prepared for the trip for a number of reasons. I had already been corresponding with people in various areas of China on iris and other plant topics for the past five years. I was also somewhat familiar with the Chinese iris flora from studying the information available in English. I offered to research the likelihood of such a trip. When I wrote to China, my associates there suggested I come the following spring. Thus the China Iris Project was born and grew very rapidly. I hoped to follow in the tradition of 19th-century plant hunters and bring back new horticultural treasures from China.

As I began, the only comprehensive work on Chinese irises was published in Chinese as part of the *Flora Reipublicae Popularis Sinicae*, a comprehensive review of all vascular plants of China. It has been published in parts for nearly 20 years; when finished, it is expected to consist of 80 volumes in 125 parts. The section on the genus *Iris* was published in 1985 in Volume 16, Part 1. The author is Zhao Yu-tang, a biology professor in Jilin Province.

As trip preparations were launched, I collected all available information on Chinese irises, made contacts with irisarians in various parts of China, and attempted to raise travel money through the China Iris Project. Ultimately this project was sponsored by 20 individuals, organizations, and institutions, but was not directly affiliated with any one public or private organization.

The collecting trip was made with the financial support of individuals and institutions in the United States, Canada, France, and China. My travel was from May 1 to May 23, 1989, and covered approximately 12,000 kilometers, nearly 7500 miles.

Just prior to my departure, headlines erupted with news about student democracy demonstrations in Beijing, but since my travels intentionally avoided stops in Beijing I was not terribly concerned and my Chinese associates convinced me that there would be no problems. The Shanghai Botanical Garden had agreed to be my official host in China, and a member of their staff, Mr. Lu Bo, accompanied me on my travels. I was also required to have a local host at each of my specific destinations in China.

A day after my arrival, Mr. Lu and I traveled by train to Hangzhou, Zhejiang Province, to visit the Botanical Garden. In China, unlike in the West, irises are grown primarily in herb gardens because of their traditional uses in herbal medicine and therapy. I observed, photographed, and made notes about cultivated irises in China. I was also able to see some species I found nowhere else in China, and the director of the Herb Garden allowed me to collect living materials of some rare species. We returned to Shanghai after a few days and deposited living collections at the Shanghai Botanical Gardens where the staff had agreed to care for plants while I was making field collections.

Without a break Mr. Lu and I flew north to Changchun, Jilin Province, to be hosted by Prof. Zhao Yu-tang and his chief graduate student, Mr. Xie Hang. One person's contribution has often been central to the history of a nation's flora; for Chinese iris, Zhao has been that person. No one in China took a comprehensive interest in the vast and varied iris flora until Zhao Yu-tang began publishing scarcely 10 years ago. Since then Zhao has traced and tracked down nearly 60 native species of iris and has described six new species and numerous new forms and varieties. He has also clarified some confusion over little-known species and brought lost species into the light of our day. Not since Peter-Simon Pallas' work more than 200 years ago have so many new Chinese species been investigated and explained. Prof. Zhao Yu-tang is the foremost Chinese iris authority of our time, and I think his stature will continue to grow as his works make their way into the English language. His work not only inspired this volume, but also has aroused new excitement over the Chinese *Iris* flora. Through his work and that of his students, such as Lu Jing-mei, Qi Yao-bin, and especially Xie Hang, the *Iris* flora of China is receiving more study than ever before.

For nearly eight days we journeyed across Jilin Province and into parts of Inner Mongolia. The expedition was at times rigorous, requiring extreme patience to conform to official regulations for foreign travelers in China. Generally, the Chinese government has designated certain cities and towns off limits to foreign travelers for a variety of reasons, but quite frequently there are simply no facilities available at the standard established for foreigners. I needed special permits to make visits into some spots, and these outings were restricted to daytime. Extended travel was not allowed, and certain locations were prohibited.

Professor Zhao, Mr. Xie, and the entire support staff of the Northeast Normal University provided assistance that was essential to the success of my travels there. I was able to collect *Iris* species in the wild in Jilin and Inner Mongolia and transport them successfully back to Shanghai for safekeeping.

Again without a break, Mr. Lu and I traveled from Shanghai west to Chengdu, the capital of China's most populous province, Sichuan. In Sichuan we were hosted by Professor Yen Chi and his wife Prof. Yang Jun-liang, both of Sichuan Agricultural University. Professor Yen is also the director of the internationally known Tritaceae Research Institute. In just over a week we traveled from low elevation along rivers into high mountains near the Tibet border. There is an extremely rich flora in this province, and iris are no exception. I was able to collect some much-sought species from truly wild locations. Travel was always by four-wheel-drive vehicles, frequently over rugged mountain roads, hazardous with mud and landslides.

We again carefully brought plants back to Shanghai, adding them to our previous collections. The staff of the Shanghai Botanical Garden assisted me in washing, labeling, and preparing the collections for inspection by Chinese agricultural authorities to obtain health and export permits.

By the time I returned to Shanghai, the student demonstrations had spread to most stops along my journey. In Shanghai the demonstrations had become large. A last-minute ticket cancellation nearly brought the entire project to a stop, but a hasty reinstatement allowed me to return to the United States with my living iris collections. In San Francisco, the United States Department of Agriculture, Office of Plant Protection and Quarantine, spent the entire day inspecting the living materials before releasing them with a clean bill of health for my final return to Kansas City.

I brought back more than 400 living *Iris* plants which were cleaned, sorted, and distributed to sponsors for eventual establishment in cultivation. Contacts and exchanges of seed and plants continue to provide further information on the iris flora of China. By late 1990 some living materials had been supplied to commercial growers specializing in *Iris* species. A list of current nursery sources appears in Appendix 6. As more of these plants are grown and propagated, even more of the newly cultivated species will be available to gardeners everywhere.

My trip was the first collection trip to China devoted specifically to observing and collecting native *Iris* species. My collections introduced more plants of more species of Chinese origin than ever before. During the trip through China, I made extensive field notes and took color slides of many species. We also collected local experiences concerning the cultivation of Chinese irises. These elements have all been refined, compiled, and expanded to make up a number of articles for iris-related journals.

In preparing these articles I saw the need for a complete translation of Professor Zhao's work on irises from the *Flora Reipublicae Popularis Sinicae*. With Zhao's approval, I contacted my friend Youngjune Chang, a graduate student of botany, to begin the project. To create Part I of this book, I expanded on the articles that I had written. Mr. Chang's translation of Zhao's work makes up Part II. To this work we have added supporting materials to comprise as complete a treatment as possible on this subject.

Part II is a literal English translation of a work that should be of interest to all who appreciate and have an affinity for Chinese *Iris*. The translation consists of the entire *Iris* text from the *Flora Reipublicae Popularis Sinicae*, rearranged in sequential form. It covers the 60 species accounts and includes 21 line drawings, originally numbered 43 through 63. The genus *Iris* is the 10th genus of the family Iridaceae to be reviewed in this volume of the *Flora*.

I reviewed, refined, and edited the translation, which underwent further review and editorial advice by Mrs. Jean Witt of Seattle, Washington. Jean's many contributions and her insight helped to make the entire translation more coherent and consistent. Brian Mathew of the Royal Botanical Garden, Kew, England, contributed an alternate translation of the key, some of which was incorporated into the present version. The entire English text was read, revised, and approved by Zhao Yu-tang. Some Russian translation in the species accounts is courtesy of my good friend Mr. Robert Fabel-Ward of Little Rock, Arkansas. Inevitable errors will occur, and I take full responsibility for the final presentation. I offer this translation in the hope that it will be of use.

Support for the translation was given by the sponsors of the

Chinese Iris Project, with special assistance from Ms. Elaine Hulbert of Floyd, Virginia, who has looked forward to this book since its inception. There has been major financial and moral support and interest from the Species Iris Group of North America, a section of the American Iris Society.

Any translation loses certain subtleties and meaning, and this work is no exception. However, we faced a particularly challenging task in the presentation of common names for Chinese iris. Most iris species do not have common names, including American and European species which are far better known. Therefore we translated the Chinese names colloquially, providing in some instances new names for commonly grown species and in others, names that simply seem quite different from accustomed English usage. This is because these are the Chinese common names, rather than the English common name for Chinese plants.

We have used the current pinyin system for the translation of place names where possible. Place names can also be further translated to reveal the meaning of the name, but in general this has not been done. Appendix 1 presents a list of transliterated Chinese common names and equivalent English translations, with some notes on these names. Appendices 2 and 3 review the distribution of Chinese iris. A glossary has been added to explain some of the technical terms. Appendix 7 is a conversion table for metric measurements.

As a student and admirer of Chinese iris, I had the opportunity to travel in parts of China and observe about half of the native species in the wild and in cultivation on their home grounds. I hope to relate my experience with these iris in the field in China and from growing many in my own garden. My wish is that this will help to introduce more gardeners to the mystery and wonder to be found in Chinese iris species. I hope this treatment will point out gaps that are in need of being filled.

Because there is no comparable volume in English on the subject of Chinese irises, this one should be considered a preliminary report. I suspect that we will learn more about the secrets of Chinese iris within the next few years, and that new species will come to light and into the West. Our understanding remains incomplete, and speculations have been based on still-sketchy information. For that I apologize in advance. I hope that this initial work will encourage further study of Chinese irises and that this book will increase interest in the irises and the iris researchers of China.

James W. Waddick

Acknowledgments

Many people and organizations made this book possible, and I wish to thank all who helped in numerous specific ways.

For fostering the idea and supporting the basic planning: James L. Murrain and Robert Pries. For providing moral support and encouragement my special gratitude to my many friends in the Greater Kansas City Iris Society. For making the trip and translation possible, all the sponsors of the China Iris Project: Alan McMurtrie (Canada); Bruce Richardson (Canada); Robert Pries; Phoebe Copley; Canadian Iris Society, Verna Laurin, president (Canada); Iris Society of Minnesota, Jack Worel, president; Joan Cooper, Mary Duval, Inge Hempl, and Jack Worel; Chicago Botanical Garden, Kris Jarantoski, assistant director; Greater St. Louis Iris Society, Mark Dienstbach, president; Species Iris Group of North America, Colin Rigby, president; Greater Kansas City Iris Society, Jim Hedgecock, president; Jean Peyrard (France); David Lennette; Bill Brobisky; King County Iris Society (Seattle, Washington), Robert Bruland, president; Elaine Hulbert; Robert Hollingworth; Darrell Probst; Claude and Joanne Derr; and Richard Kiyomoto. For additional financial assistance: Kansas City Garden Club, Dolores Denney, and the Iris Society of Minnesota. For assisting with plant distributions: Donna Aldridge and Faye Carpenter of the Greater Kansas City Iris Society.

In China there are many people and institutions to thank. The Shanghai Botanical Garden was my official host while I was in China. They facilitated all travel arrangements and official clearances; my special thanks to their Director Zhang Lian-quan, the Vice Director Luo Guo-xiong, the Director Emeritus Wang Dajun, and the entire staff. For their personal help and attention to countless details, thanks to Ms. Chen Nian-nian and Ms. Lu Ming-zhen. The trip would have been impossible without the help and friendship of my assistant, traveling companion, and friend, Mr. Lu Bo, who made all the pieces fit together.

I would like to thank the staff of the Hangzhou Botanical Garden and especially Director Yu Zhi-zhou and High Engineer

Lin Yun-foo. Special thanks to my friend and the curator of their wonderful bamboo garden, Mr. Zheng Xing-yu who was my official host. Special thanks also to Ms. Lin Jin-zhen, director of the herb garden, and her assistant Ms. Li Jing-jen.

In Jilin Province I had the extreme good fortune to meet and travel with the man who put all the iris of China into perspective, Prof. Zhao Yu-tang, professor of biology at Northeast Normal University. He was an inspiration for the trip and an endless source of information, a good traveling companion, and a model of scholarship. My thanks to his departmental chairperson, Ms. He Mengyuan, for allowing him to escape his university teaching duties during my stay in Jilin. Special thanks to Mr. Xie Hang, the chief successor and prize student of Professor Zhao. Mr. Xie is a talented botanist and expert field scientist.

Many thanks to my Sichuan hosts, Prof. Yen Chi and his wife Prof. Yang Jun-liang, both of the Sichuan Agricultural University. Professor Yen is also director of the Tritaceae Research Institute. Thanks also to his prime student of iris, Mr. Zhou Yau-dong.

Special thanks also for the hospitality and help of Mr. Qiu Fu-geng, director of the Zhejiang Forestry Institute; Mr. Tong Yu-lin, vice director of the Foreign Affairs Office of Wulanhot, Inner Mongolia; Mr. Ni Kan, director of bamboo, Shanghai Botanical Garden; and Timothy Torbett, USDA, PPQ, San Francisco.

The Species Iris Group of North America, a section of the American Iris Society, provided direct and indirect help in too many ways to delineate, but they were involved and influential in almost every part of the trip and in the completion of this report. Their moral and financial support were crucial to the completion of this project. Powell Gardens of Kingsville, Missouri, has been interested in the project and provided financial support. My thanks to their board of trustees and the staff. To the many others who helped out in a variety of ways, I give my sincere gratitude.

James W. Waddick

PART I

Chinese Iris in the Wild and in the Garden

by

James W. Waddick

FIGURE 1   *Pardanthopsis dichotoma* – The widely known and grown Vesper Iris blooms in late summer on tall, wiry flower stems. The wild forms are duller in color than this bright lilac cultivated variety. It is native to a very harsh climate in northeast China. PHOTO BY J. WADDICK

FIGURE 2   *Iris tectorum* – Widely cultivated in China, *I. tectorum* is the commonest of all Chinese irises. The casual visitor will find this plant blooming in window boxes, planters, and small house gardens across the nation. This photo was taken near Woolong in central Sichuan, China. PHOTO BY J. WADDICK

FIGURE 3 *Iris chrysographes* – This nearly black species of Siberian iris is admired for the intense color and bright gold signal marks. This cultivated plant shows the deep color, but variants include nearly red flowers and a range of smoky purples marked with varying amounts of gold lines on the falls.

FIGURE 4 *Iris confusa* – *Iris confusa* is common in corn and wheat fields where it grows to 1.5 m (5 ft) or more in height and produces a network of rhizomes that sprout readily even after field cultivation. This pale lilac-blue color is the most common form. Here it is growing in late May on the slopes of Mt. Niba, Sichuan, at over 1000 meters. PHOTO BY J. WADDICK

FIGURE 5   *Iris delavayi* – The wide petals, rich purple color, and white signals on tall flower stems all help to identify Iris delavayi. This plant grown from seed collected in northern Yunnan Province is cultivated in the University of California Botanic Garden in Berkeley, California. This is a Chinese member of the Siberian iris group. PHOTO BY S. HOGAN

FIGURE 6   *Iris formosana* – This seems to be the only iris species native to the island of Taiwan and therefore qualifies as a truly tropical iris. This is a cultivated plant with broad white flowers marked in yellow. The plant form is similar to the closely related *I. japonica*; however, *I. formosana* flowers are larger and fewer in number. PHOTO BY J. WADDICK

FIGURE 7   *Iris sichuanensis* – One of the largest pseudoregelia irises, *Iris sichuanensis* may be a form of the more widely distributed *I. leptophylla*. The flowers, in a variety of shades, are shown here in late May near the town of Wen Chuan, Sichuan Province. PHOTO BY J. WADDICK

FIGURE 8   *Iris speculatrix* – The subject of much speculation, *Iris speculatrix* may belong in the *Chinenses* series also. It has delicate flowers with bright signals and rings on the falls. It is apparently widely distributed in eastern China from Hong Kong north beyond Shanghai. It has been erroneously known as *Iris grijsi* in the literature. PHOTO BY J. WADDICK

FIGURE 9 *Iris wilsonii* – One of two yellow-flowered Chinese Siberian iris species, *Iris wilsonii* has large flowers with angled standards. All species of Chinese Siberian iris with 40 chromosomes hybridize readily in cultivation. Pure species can easily be lost as vigorous self-sown hybrid seedlings can crowd out choice parent plants.
PHOTO BY C. MCGAVRAN

FIGURE 10 *Pardanthopsis dichotoma—Habitat* – These low, barren hills of southeast Inner Mongolia are the home of *Pardanthopsis dichotoma*. Here in early May the plants are just emerging from the ground and only 5–7 cm (2 to 3 in) in height. This climate has low rainfall and cold winters with no snow cover. Intense summer heat and full sun are no problem for these sturdy, undemanding iris relatives. PHOTO BY J. WADDICK

FIGURE 11   *Iris sanguinea* – This is the Chinese member of the Siberian iris group, found near damp sites in northeast China. The heavily veined hafts are characteristic of wild plants, such as this growing in the Changbai Mountains of Jilin Province. PHOTO BY Y. T. ZHAO

FIGURE 12   *Iris typhifolia* – Recently introduced into cultivation after remaining a mystery for years, *Iris typhifolia* is believed to be closely related to the garden Siberian irises with 28 chromosomes. This is the first bloom seen in Western cultivation, in the green-house of R. Wise of the British Iris Society. This iris promises to be very popular in many home gardens.
PHOTO BY P. MAYNARD

FIGURE 13   *Iris minutoaurea* – The marked yellow flowers of *Iris minutoaurea* are the smallest of any cultivated species. Pictured blooming in Missouri, it grows in continental climates that show extreme seasonality and rainfall. Perhaps the most common of the series *Chinenses*, it is still rare in cultivation.
PHOTO BY J. WADDICK

FIGURE 14   *Iris rossii* – This is a rare species in China, found only in southern Liaoning Province where this photo was taken. *Iris rossii* is a seldom-cultivated member of the series *Chineses* and is also found in Korea and Japan.
PHOTO BY Y. T. ZHAO

FIGURE 15 *Iris tenuifolia* – The species of the series *Tenuifoliae*, here represented by *Iris tenuifolia*, are all poorly known. This species grows in a harsh climate in compacted loess soils, and it dies down to ground level or below in winter. The thin rounded leaves continue to grow at the onset of mild weather. It is a difficult species to cultivate and will remain a curiosity rather than a garden standby. This plant growing near Bai Cheng, Jilin Province, blooms in mid-May. PHOTO BY J. WADDICK

FIGURE 16 *Iris ventricosa* – Although *Iris ventricosa* is related to *Iris tenuifolia,* it is more attractive and easier to cultivate. The inflated bracts below each flower are significant and distinctive. This plant blooms in mid-May. It is shown growing on the grounds of a monument to Genghis Khan near the center of Ulanhot, Inner Mongolia. PHOTO BY J. WADDICK

FIGURE 17   *Iris ruthenica* – This small species has a wide northern distribution beyond China west to eastern Europe. The form pictured here is *I. ruthenica* var. *nana* blooming nearly at ground level on short flower stems. The typical form has flowers held about 10 cm (4 in) above ground. PHOTO BY J. WADDICK

FIGURE 18   *Iris uniflora* – Growing on rocky hillsides, *Iris uniflora* is a common spring wildflower in northeast China. I was surprised to see it growing in the boulevard parkways in Changchun City. As the name suggests, there is a single flower on each fan of foliage. Wild variants range from near white through purple and reddish purple. PHOTO BY J. WADDICK

FIGURE 19   *Iris mandshurica* – This small pseudoregelia species grows over a fairly wide area in northeast China. Like all pseudoregelias, it forms a tight clump, growing and spreading slowly. In early May this species blooms a few kilometers from the capital city of Changchun, Jilin Province, China.
PHOTO BY J. WADDICK

FIGURE 20   *Iris tigridia* – The unique color patterns of *Iris tigridia* offer a sharp contrast to most pseudoregelia irises. This species grows under conditions of low rainfall and extremes of both winter and summer temperatures in Inner Mongolia. A few color variants are known from wild populations. It is very uncommon in cultivation. PHOTO BY J. WADDICK

FIGURE 21   *Iris laevigata* – Among the loveliest of all water irises, this species frequently dominates swampy sites in the far north. A few cultivated varieties are grown in ponds as it is the most water loving of all iris species. PHOTOGRAPHED IN DAIQINGGOU, INNER MONGOLIA, BY Y. T. ZHAO

FIGURE 22   *Iris setosa* – Although this iris has a wide distribution, in China it is found only in the isolated Changbai Mountains near the border between Jilin Province and North Korea. This photo was taken above an altitude of 1500 m (5000 ft) in Changbai. The reduced standards are typical of the species, but this form has very colorful style arms. PHOTO BY Y. T. ZHAO

FIGURE 23   *Iris flavissima* – Glowing like a shot of gold in a sand pile near the fields of Farmers' Professional College, *Iris flavissima* is the most eastern of all *Psammiris* species. This location, near the village of Shan Men in Jilin Province, China, is less than 50 km from the border of Heilongjiang Province. Photo taken the first week of May at the onset of flowering.
PHOTO BY J. WADDICK

FIGURE 24   *Iris forrestii* – The other yellow-flowered Chinese Siberian iris species, *Iris forrestii* has erect standards and smaller flowers than *I. wilsonii*. Care must be taken to prevent bee hybridization with other species of this series. This species grows well in the mild climate of the Seattle, Washington, area. PHOTO BY C. MCGAVRAN

FIGURE 25   *Iris wattii* – Known as the Bamboo Iris, *I. wattii* lives up to its common name with canes up to 2.7 m (9 ft) tall and masses of pale lilac flowers. It is a close relative to *Iris confusa* and *I. japonica,* but poorly known in the wild. This photo was taken in the Kunming Institute of Botany in Yunnan, China. PHOTO BY N. TRACK

FIGURE 26   *Iris collettii* – This rare iris is a member of the subgenus *Nepalensis.* It has large tuberous roots and a small, nearly nonexistent rhizome. Not in cultivation, these flowers were photographed near Gang Ho Bang, Lijiang (Dayan) in northwest Yunnan. PHOTO BY N. TRACK

FIGURE 27   *Iris decora* – Common and widely cultivated, *Iris decora* is the only other member of the subgenus *Nepalensis*. This is generally easy to grow, but it blooms for a short period, and the foliage is equally fleeting. The plant pictured thrives in Missouri with little care and is easily grown from seed.
PHOTO BY J. WADDICK

FIGURE 28   *Iris kemaonensis* – This dwarf pseudoregelia iris adapts well to cultivation. This plant thrives in Virginia and is shown blooming in May.
PHOTO BY E. HULBERT

FIGURE 29   *Iris japonica* f. *pallescens* – Introduced to the Western world from Japan, *Iris japonica* f. *pallescens* is common in mild parts of China. As seen growing here at the Lushan Botanical Garden in Jiangxi Province, this is a crested iris with many flowers per flower stalk and glossy deep green leaves.
PHOTO BY Y. T. ZHAO

FIGURE 30   *Iris lactea* var. *chinensis* – This distinctive species is equally at home at the roadside or in overcultivated fields across China. It has been misidentified and sold as a variety of other species' names, but once known and grown it is always recognizable. This plant blooms near a mud slide on the road to Song Pan, Sichuan, in mid-May. PHOTO BY J. WADDICK

FIGURE 31   *Iris sichuanensis—Habitat – Iris sichuanensis* can be seen growing in a small pocket of soil on the nearly vertical rock walls of the upper Min River valley. Differences in exposure, prevailing wind, and rainfall in these mountains produce a patchwork of suitable growing pockets. PHOTO BY J. WADDICK

1. Chinese Species in Their Native Habitats

China has been called the "Mother of Gardens" because of all the plants collected from that country and introduced into horticulture in the West. Some of the world's best known and most loved garden plants are native to China. This is not, however, the case with irises. The majority of the horticulturally well-known irises are bearded species and their hybrids derived from species native to the Near East and Europe. China has contributed nothing to the wealth of cultivated bearded iris in our gardens, but more beardless species in greater variety are distributed in China than anywhere else.

The genus *Iris* consists of approximately 300 species. The divisions within the genus have been clarified in the excellent recent works of G. I. Rodionenko and B. Mathew. The structure of the genus can be simplified as follows:

Genus *Iris*
    Subgenus *Iris* (bearded or pogon iris)
        Section *Iris* (bearded iris)
        Section *Psammiris* (sand iris)
        Section *Oncocyclus* (oncocyclus or aril iris)
        Section *Hexapogon*
        Section *Regelia* (regelia iris)
        Section *Pseudoregelia* (pseudoregelia iris)
    Subgenus *Limniris* (beardless or apogon iris)
        Section *Lophiris* (crested or Evansia iris)
        Section *Limniris* (beardless or apogon irise with 16 series worldwide, 8 in China
        Section *Ophioiris*
    Subgenus *Nepalensis*
    Subgenus *Xiphium* (Dutch and other related bulbous iris)
    Subgenus *Scorpiris* (juno iris)
    Subgenus *Hermodactyloides* (reticulata and other related bulbous iris)

Obviously not all of these divisions occur in China. The bulbous iris are notably absent. The genus *Iris* is clearly related to the genus *Pardanthopsis,* as indicated by the frequent inclusion of the species *P. dichotoma* (Figure 1) in the genus *Iris,* a practice followed by Professor Zhao. The genera *Belamcanda* and *Hermodactylus* are also close relatives.

The true *Iris* species are typically north temperate plants. The greatest concentration of species is found in the Near and Middle East. The largest group of iris is the bearded iris subgenus which is centered in this area. Various beardless iris are distributed north to arctic regions, and many others are found at extremely high elevations. Although no iris can truly be called "tropical," several Chinese species' distributions extend into the northern edge of the Tropical Zone.

China is the home of more than 60 species, forms, and varieties of wild irises discovered and named over the past 200 years. In comparison, the North American continent has fewer than 30 and Europe has approximately 25 native species. Some of the beardless Chinese irises have found their way into discriminating gardens, including the wealth of Siberian species and hybrids, crested iris—especially *Iris tectorum* (Figure 2)—and a number of water iris (most of the series *Laevigatae* are found in or near water). However, few cultivated irises in horticulture today are actually of Chinese origin. Many of the common species of iris native to China have been introduced from countries other than China, such as Japan, Korea, and Russia.

China itself has a long history of cultivation of its native plants. Some plants, such as azaleas, camellias, peonies, and some flowering trees, have been domesticated and hybridized for centuries and are well known and long revered. Irises have not figured heavily in Chinese horticultural history, but more in the history of herbal medicines. The numerous important herbal uses of irises include both internal and external preparations from many species. The distribution of widely used species has undoubtedly been affected by their cultivation for medicinal uses.

China has been a land of mystery to most Westerners for centuries. It is the embodiment of the mysterious East, yet it has many ties to the West. It has been the source of commercial treasures from the earliest silk and spice trades to essentials of the modern world. As a large north temperate nation it has numerous inherent similarities to the industrialized cities and nations of the northern hemisphere.

China is the second largest country in the world. It spans an area from beyond 50° north latitude to below the Tropic of Cancer. Altitudes range from 150 m (more than 500 ft) below sea level to the world's tallest peak, 8700 m (over 29,000 ft) above the sea. It is bounded by the Pacific Ocean on the east and crossed by some of the world's largest rivers. Understandably China has a wide range of environments, from desert to jungle and mountain meadow to temperate forest. Many northern parts have been glaciated. China has a rich and varied flora including many ancient elements.

It can easily be said that most of the native irises are found only in China and that some groups within the genus are restricted to China and its immediate surroundings. If many of the names in the following pages seem quite strange even to students of iris, this only emphasizes our unfamiliarity with the large and varied Chinese flora.

Our understanding of Chinese iris is based primarily on a few almost random collections by plant hunters in China over the past two centuries and on Chinese species that were first observed and collected in Japan. The Chinese plant collections consist of herbarium specimens gathered opportunistically as the plants were found in flower. Western knowledge of some Chinese species is based solely on these few dried herbarium sheets. Other Chinese iris collections consist of plants found in seed, grown to maturity, and then named or identified. Very few Chinese irises were identified in the field, collected as living materials, and introduced into horticulture prior to my trip. Japanese plants of Chinese origin have little or no scientific value in explaining much about the nature of Chinese irises in the wild. Today there are very few clear and documented observations of Chinese iris in their natural habitat and none over the whole distribution of any one species.

DISTRIBUTION, ECOLOGY, AND ENVIRONMENT

The distribution of Chinese iris is poorly documented in spotty and uneven records and thus very poorly known. Collections have been made from surprisingly few locations. No Western scientist and few Chinese scientists have made extensive studies of the Chinese field collections in Chinese herbaria. General records of distributions are available by province for most species, but specific localities are rarely mentioned. Anecdotal accounts of species in the wild must be considered with some doubt because of the numerous incorrect identifications. Even in the world's largest herbarium collections where specimens have been studied and reviewed, many unidentified specimens remain, as do many for which no specific locations have been noted. Herbarium specimens tend to be only plants in flower, perhaps because Chinese irises seem to have been collected by coincidence: a collector finds a plant blooming, is taken by its beauty, and then collects herbarium specimens. Some species' distributions seem uneven and have great gaps, but this may be due to uneven collecting or simply to the lack of material for many locations. The distribution information given below is based on what is known today. Aggressive new collections and thorough scientific review of existing Chinese herbarium materials may shed new light on actual distributions.

A province-by-province distribution of Chinese iris species appears in Appendix 3. I have used the current (pinyin) characterizations for location names in China and include as Appendix 2 a chart that compares these various provincial names. A map of China appears in Appendix 4 with province names. At first mention, the official full name of a province appears in parentheses, after its more commonly used, usually shortened, name. I have not attempted to give old and new names for specific locations except for the few cases in which well-known alternate names (in parentheses) follow the current name.

In considering the distribution of Chinese species, I have taken the widest possible view of China, including both Hong Kong and Taiwan, which are floristically part of the entire China complex. Japan and Korea also share most of their iris floras with that of China, although each has a single endemic species. Korea is the only known home of *Iris odaesanensis* in the *Chinenses* series. It is confined to Mount Odaesan in Korea. Japan is the only known home of *Iris gracilipes,* a small woodland species of crested iris found in the mountains of all three main islands. There are no known *Iris* species native to China's largest island, Hainan, in the South China Sea. China also has numerous ties to the northern floras of Mongolia and the USSR, as well as to the southwest floras of Burma, Bangladesh, India, Bhutan, and Nepal.

Fourteen divisions (subgenera, sections, and series) of the genus *Iris* are found in China. Most of these are centered in China, obviously their original center of distribution. Among the bearded iris (subgenus *Iris*) are included the *Psammiris* or sand iris with all known species found in China and the pseudoregelias with all but two of the species from China. Among the crested iris, all Asian species except for the one Japanese endemic are found in China. All but one of the *Chinenses* series of iris, the Korean endemic, are found here, as well as two of the three *Ruthenicae* series. The

Siberian irises are all native to China except for the type species, *Iris sibirica*, but China seems clearly to be their home. Half of the world's water iris (series *Laevigateae*) are found here and every species in the series *Tenuifoliae*. A number of other iris divisions are represented here by one or two species, but only one section is totally endemic: the unique *I. anguifuga*.

China is the only known home of the following species of irises: *I. anguifuga*, *I. bulleyana*, *I. cathayensis*, *I. chrysographes* (Figure 3), *I. curvifolia*, *I. confusa* (Figure 4), *I. delavayi* (Figure 5), *I. farreri*, *I. formosana* (Figure 6), *I. henryi*, *I. kobayashii*, *I. latistyla*, *I. leptophylla*, *I. narcissiflora*, *I. pandurata*, *I. polysticta*, *I. proantha*, *I. qinghainica*, *I. sichuanensis* (Figure 7), *I. speculatrix* (Figure 8), *I. subdichotoma*, and *I. wilsonii* (Figure 9).

There are four major regions of iris distribution in China: the northeast, north central, east central, and the southwest regions. The provinces of Heilongjiang (Heilongkiang), Jilin (Kirin), and Liaoning in the northeast account for 19 or almost a third of the species. The north central provinces of Gansu (Kansu), Ningxia (Ninghsia Hui Autonomous Region or Ningxia Huizu Zizhiqu), and Shaanxi (Shenhsi) can claim an additional 17 species. A smaller group of species is found in eastern central China around Zhejiang (Chekiang), Jiangsu (Kiangsu), and Anhui (Anwei) provinces. In the southwest the mountainous provinces of Tibet (Tibet Autonomous Region or Xizang Zizhiqu), Yunnan, and Sichuan (Szechwan) account for 27 species, nearly half of all those in China.

Northeast China Region

The provinces of Heilongjiang, Jilin, Liaoning, and eastern portions of Inner Mongolia (Nei Menggu Zizhiqu or Inner Mongolia Autonomous Region) are characterized by low mountains and plateaus (Figure 10). The main vegetation is mixed northern broadleaf deciduous hardwoods and coniferous forests, but there are also dry prairies and near desert. The climate is extremely cold in the winter with lows to −29° C (−20° F) or lower and summer heat to more than 38° C (100° F). Rainfall is spring seasonal and, especially in inland areas, quite low. Vegetation has many affinities with the north temperate flora and specific ties to eastern North America and northern Asia. The entire region has been glaciated, and soil types reflect this fact.

Among the19 species of iris in this region, the following are most indicative of this distribution center: *Iris sanguinea* (Figure 11), *I. typhifolia* (Figure 12) (*Sibiricae*); *I. minutoaurea* (Figure 13), *I.*

rossii (Figure 14) (*Chinenses*); *I. bungei, I. kobayashi, I. loczyi, I. tenuifolia* (Figure 15), *I. ventricosa* (Figure 16) (*Tenuifoliae*); *I. ruthenica* (Figure 17), and *I. uniflora* (Figure 18) (*Ruthenicae*). The species found only in this area include *I. kobayashi, I. maackii, I. mandshurica* (Figure 19), *I. minutoaurea, I. rossii, I. tigridia* (Figure 20), *I. typhifolia,* and *I. ventricosa.* The only species endemic to this region is *Iris kobayashii;* all other species are found in neighboring areas of Russia or North Korea.

The most characteristic irises comprise one of two ecological groups. One group is found growing in cold dry areas. These species are extremely hardy and resistant to many ecological hardships. They include those species in the series *Ruthenicae, Tenuifoliae,* and *Chinenses.* The second smaller group is associated with water, either permanent swamps and rivers or more temporary streams and seasonally wet spots. These iris include the two Siberian species indicated above plus the water irises *I. ensata, I. laevigata* (Figure 21), and *I. maackii.* These tend to be large, vigorous plants that can take advantage of seasonally wet places. Seeds are easily transported, and new plants grow quickly to maturity. The European *I. pseudacorus* is naturalized in this region.

The most widely distributed iris of the northern hemisphere, *Iris setosa* (Figure 22), is found in the northeast China region confined to the higher elevations of the Changbai Mountains of southeast Jilin Province. It is also found in adjacent border areas of North Korea. This species is distributed from the eastern third of Canada and the adjacent northeastern portions of the United States, then skips westward to Alaska and across the Bering Straits to various spots in north central Asia, down to northern parts of Japan, and into its small area of distribution in China.

Iris sanguinea has a wide disjunction in its distribution. Beyond the appropriate environments in Liaoning Province, it has also been located approximately 1300 km (800 miles) to the south in the Yixing (Ishing) area around Lake Tai (Tai Hu) in southern Jiangsu Province. No crested irises are native to the northeast China region although *I. tectorum* can be cultivated here.

North Central China Region

This region of China is centered around the provinces of Gansu, Ningxia, and Shaanxi, but includes areas of Xinjiang (Xinjiang Weiwu-er Zizhiqu) and Qinghai (Tsinghai) to the west, and western parts of Inner Mongolia to the east. The area is characterized by high rugged mountains, high plateaus, and mountain basins. Most areas are quite dry; in the north and east this region abuts the great Gobi Desert. Temperatures range from winter lows of −30° C (−20° F) to summer highs of 38° C (100° F) or higher. The vegetation consists mainly of grasslands with some broadleaf deciduous forest areas and montane vegetation. The flora has affinities primarily with northern Asia and northeast China as well as with Mongolia and the USSR.

There are approximately 20 species in the region depending on how it is defined. The most typical iris of this region are: *I. bungei, I. farreri, I. polysticta, I. qinghainica, I. songarica, I. tenuifolia* (series *Tenuifoliae*); *I. halophila* (series *Spuriae*); *I. goniocarpa, I. pandurata* (section *Pseudoregelia*); *I. curvifolia, I. flavissima* (Figure 23), and *I. potaninii* (Section Psammiris). The species found only in this distribution center are *I. curvifolia, I. halophila, I. pandurata, I. potaninii, I. qinghainica,* and *I. scariosa*. The endemic species are *I. curvifolia, I. pandurata,* and *I. qinghainica*.

The species are generally those typical of high dry mountain plains and intermontane meadows and valleys. These are very hardy, durable plants capable of withstanding extremes of temperature and rainfall. Many species such as *I. songarica* and *I. halophila* have affinities to the Russian steppes and further west. Most of the iris species are relatively small, sturdy plants with thin drought-resistant leaves. No water irises are found in the north central China region; and of the widespread Siberian series, only *I. wilsonii* occurs, and this only in favorable locations.

This region includes some species that are at the extremes of the distributions for their group, such as *I. halophila,* the most eastern spuria iris, and *I. scariosa,* the most eastern bearded iris (section *Iris*). Most *Iris* species in this distribution center are poorly known in the wild, in the world's herbaria, and in horticulture. Few of these species in cultivation are from plant materials originating in China.

East Central China Region

This is a broad region of China centered on the coastal provinces of Zhejiang and Jiangsu, and the interior province of Anhui, but extending beyond to encompass parts of Hunan, Hubei (Hopei or Hopeh), and Fujian (Fukien) provinces. This is a broad area of low plains and hills. Elevations are generally under 500 m (1600 ft). The climate is temperate but quite moderate, with winter temperatures below freezing and moderate-to-warm summer highs. Rainfall is generally abundant; the entire region in many ways parallels the eastern seaboard of the United States. The vegetation is quite varied with mixed broadleaf and coniferous evergreens, wide belts of broadleaf deciduous forest, and expansive cultivated tracts. Major population centers are found in the east central China region.

This is the smallest and most diffuse of the iris regions in China. Approximately 13 species are found here. Few can be considered distinctive for this region, but I include the following: *I. anguifuga, I. cathayensis, I. proantha*, and *I. speculatrix*. These represent various groups within the genus, and all but *I. speculatrix* are endemic to this region.

Ecologically the iris of this region can be called woodland and forest-edge species. They live in temperate to mild temperate climates with sufficient seasonal rainfall. They do not show specific adaptations to drought or other climatic extremes. The exception is the recently described and somewhat bizarre *Iris anguifuga*. This odd iris goes completely dormant during the summer and is atypical of all other iris in the region. It has also been assigned to a unique division within the genus.

The other oddity in the region is *I. sanguinea* var. *yixingensis*. This is a Siberian iris variety with a disjunct population in southern Jiangsu Province, approximately 1300 km (800 miles) south of the main distribution in the northeast. Attempts to relocate this iris have been in vain. It may have been eliminated in recent times, or perhaps it was a collection anomaly.

Southwest China Region

This is an extremely large distribution center in terms of geographic area and number of iris. It is centered in the provinces of Sichuan, Yunnan, and Tibet, with adjacent areas of Guizhou (Kweichow) Province. This region has a variety of environments and climates. The topography ranges from low altitude plains through moderate to high mountain peaks. Climates are generally temperate but range from near tropical to areas of permanent ice and snow at the highest elevations. Rainfall is quite generous with some seasonality, but there is no extended dry season. This is the cloudiest area of China, with the largest number of foggy days and lowest number of hours of sunshine per year. Generally there are neither extremely hot nor dry areas, and the mild springlike climates favor a wide variety of vegetation. Here you can find a wide range of plants, from the tender palms and bananas at low elevations to temperate forests of deciduous and evergreen species and high alpine vegetation. The floral affinities are not as well marked as in other areas because they include ties with so many other vegetation types: temperate, tropical, and alpine.

The distinctive feature of the southwest China region is the huge Sichuan Basin. This relatively broad, flat area of hundreds of square kilometers is surrounded on all sides by protective mountains. It was a haven from Pleistocene glaciation and a refuge for temperate species of plants and animals. It is the last and only remaining home for such well-known "living fossil" species as the Dawn Redwood (*Metasequoia*), *Ginkgo,* and Giant Panda. Today it is the center of an area for mild-climate plants and animals found nowhere else.

This region accounts for 28 iris species or nearly half of those found in all of China. The distinctive species include: *Iris bulleyana, I. chrysographes, I. clarkei, I. delavayi, I. forrestii* (Figure 24), *I. phragmitetorum, I. wilsonii* (series Sibiricae); *I. farreri, I. polysticta* (series *Tenuifoliae*); *I. confusa, I. latistyla, I. milesii, I. wattii* (Figure 25) (section *Lophiris*); *I. subdichotoma* (section *Lophiris* ?); *I. collettii* (Figure 26), *I. decora* (Figure 27) (subgenus *Nepalensis*); and *I. dolichosiphon, I. goniocarpa, I. kemaonensis* (Figure 28), *I. narcissiflora, I. sichuanensis* (section *Pseudoregelia*). The species found only in this area are: *I. collettii, I. decora, I. dolichosiphon, I. farreri, I. kemaonensis, I. latistyla, I. milesii, I. narcissiflora, I. polysticta, I. subdichotoma, I. wattii,* and all of the Siberians (except *I. wilsonii*). The endemic species are limited to: *I. bulleyana, I. chrysographes, I. delavayi, I. farreri, I. latistyla, I. narcissiflora, I. phragmitetorum, I. polysticta, I. subdichotoma,* and *I. wilsonii.*

The irises of the southwest China region may be characterized as species that revel in mild temperate climates with abundant water. There are also many species that demand excellent drainage and are typical of mountain and scree situations. This region has more endemic species than any other region and is the center for the group known as the Sino-Siberian irises. These irises are widely grown although poorly known in the wild. Many species have trans-Himalayan ranges that extend south and west to India, Nepal, Burma, and Bhutan.

This region also has a large share of extremely poorly known species such as *I. farreri, I. latistyla, I. narcissiflora, I. phragmitetorum,* and *I. polysticta.* Although this region has been the center for much plant exploration and collection, it remains a treasure trove for new collections, selections, and probably new species. *Iris* species collected from the southwest China region have generally resulted from collections targeted on other groups of plants.

Pan-Chinese Species

A few species cross most distribution centers and climatic zones. These common species grow in many climates and are well known in the West. These are *Iris japonica* (Figure 29), *I. lactea* (Figure 30), *I. ruthenica, I. tectorum,* and *Pardanthopsis dichotoma.* Of these, only *Iris japonica* has a restricted southern distribution and is not found in the northern provinces. The most widespread species is *Iris lactea,* an invasive plant that colonizes waste places and lands that are no longer used for cultivation. It is widespread from Heilongjiang in the northeast to Sichuan in the southwest. It has been collected in all but six of China's provinces (primarily in extremely southern near-tropical areas). It is also widespread in Korea, India, Mongolia, and the USSR. Perhaps the most widely grown Chinese species is *Iris tectorum,* the second most widespread species in China. Its Chinese common name is simply "Iris" and it can be seen in gardens, window boxes, and by the roadside. *Iris tectorum* is not naturally found in the driest and coldest provinces, although it is quite hardy in cultivation. *Iris japonica* and *I. tectorum* are often seen planted along urban gardens and as landscaping materials.

Iris ruthenica is a northern species with an apparently uneven distribution from eastern Europe to eastern China. It is a highly variable species, and various forms have been named. *Pardanthopsis dichotoma* is widespread across northern China into Mongolia and Siberia in dry scrub areas. Formerly classified as a member of the genus *Iris,* it has too many distinctive characteristics to keep that designation.

Introduced Species

At least five widespread species are grown and naturalized in China, including *Iris × germanica, I. pallida, I. pseudacorus, I. sibirica,* and *I. versicolor.* The bearded species and their cultivars are grown in many gardens of eastern China. The Siberian iris cultivars are also cultivated. *Iris pseudacorus* and *I. versicolor* are widely cultivated and naturalized. All of these species are vigorous and adaptable. I have also seen iris collections in botanical gardens that include cultivars of spuria, Louisiana, and other species iris. These are generally found in urban botanical gardens, research gardens, and display collections. *Iris* appear not to be as widely cultivated in China as they are in the West.

The Asian American Alliance

The literature on plant geography describes numerous floral ties between eastern portions of China and the United States. Frequent examples show plant distributions limited to these two areas. In some cases the only species in a genus are found in eastern North America and in eastern Asia (*Gymnocladus, Liriodendron,* and *Nyssa*), or there may be concentrations of "parallel" species in the two areas (*Magnolia*), or there may be comparable closely related genera such as the American Bald Cypress (*Taxodium*) and the Chinese Dawn Redwood (*Metasequoia*). Similar examples can be found in many other woody trees and shrubs and in a wide variety of herbaceous perennials.

Iris are no exception. North America and China share species in each of the following groups: section *Lophiris* (crested iris), series *Tripetalae* (*I. setosa*), and series *Laevigatae* (water irises). The crested iris of North America are in two distinct groups. In the eastern half of the United States, we have the common *I. cristata* and the closely related *I. lacustris* with a very limited distribution. The very rare *I. tenuis* is restricted to a small area in the Pacific Northwest. The eastern and western species do not seem to be closely related to each other. The more numerous Chinese crested iris species form at least three distinct subgroups. The affinity of the three American species to any Chinese species is unknown and unclear at present, although hybridization tests and laboratory and field study could clarify these distinctions. *Iris setosa* is the only species found in both the United States and China, but it is widespread in other countries and fairly variable. In general its distribution suggests only the tenacity of this species to survive in harsh environments. Only the series *Laevigatae* or water iris show some interesting ties between China and North America. Each location has two common species, and most species share many specific habitat requirements. Most of the species have been successfully hybridized with each other, although hybrids are generally sterile. The Chinese and American species are indications of floral alliances in the genus. Oddly, the only other species in this series, and probably the most successful, is the European *Iris pseudacorus*.

Some other parallels are often cited, but they are of dubious reliability, such as the comparisons between *I. verna* and *I. ruthenica*, small violet-flowered plants of outwardly similar stature. Comparisons have also been drawn between the series *Californicae* and the Sino-Siberian groups, both of which have 40 chromosomes and produce viable hybrids. Even the distinctive *Iris lactea* and *I. missouriensis* have been considered as having some ties, but close examination reveals very few similarities. In general these comparisons are based on superficial similarities of gross anatomy or environmental preference and do not reveal any further true alliances.

Although there are many examples of floral ties between China and the United States, those found in the genus *Iris* are few and fairly weak. This suggests that any ties between the two locations may be very ancient, and that the species have evolved drastically enough to obliterate strong resemblances. The fact that the two locations share so few pairs of species also indicates distances in both time and space.

SYSTEMATICS

Many Chinese species are poorly known in the world's herbaria and are equally poorly known in cultivation and in the wild. It follows that their relationships to each other and to the world's iris flora in general are only partially understood. Some speculation on this situation follows.

Early plant collectors in China tended to collect certain target species, genera, or types, primarily centering on woody plants such as flowering shrubs: rhododendrons, flowering trees, and the like. *Iris* were collected as an afterthought when available, perhaps only when a plant in bloom attracted a collector's attention. Many of the earliest iris collections were small and consisted of only a few flowering specimens and from only a few areas. There have been no comprehensive iris collections in China. Until my travels in 1989, I knew of no comparable wide-ranging collections in China focused on this genus except for the work of Prof. Zhao Yu-tang and his associates in the northeastern provinces.

In addition to this meager representation of Chinese iris in herbarium collections, a number of specimens are misidentified and misunderstood. Collection information on these specimens is often scanty and incomplete. Even today there are very few qualified scientists who have seen many Chinese iris specimens and fewer still who have seen living materials. There are few laboratory reports concerning cell biology, karyotype, genetics, or other modern attempts to look at systematics of this genus in China. Most of our knowledge of the better-known species of Chinese *Iris* comes from material introduced from countries other than China.

As a result, attempts at organizing Chinese species into a

systematic arrangement have produced many educated guesses and as many educated errors. The suggestions that follow are based as much upon guesswork and speculation as upon facts and experience. Yet this analysis also includes some newly available information, based on living materials and recent collections.

Subgenus *Iris*

Of the Chinese bearded iris species, only one, *Iris scariosa,* is a typical dwarf bearded species (subgenus *Iris,* section *Iris*). It is essentially a Russian species that extends its range east through the Tian Shan Mountains and into adjacent parts of northwest China (Xinjiang Province). It is a small iris and neither well known nor widely grown.

All other native bearded species fall into two groups which are easily defined and separated based on gross physical characteristics. The psammiris or sand iris (section *Psammiris*) are a small group of species that are stoloniferous, have arillate seeds, and display beards only on the falls. The flowers tend to be clear without streaks, mottling, or stripes. The second, larger group of bearded species is in the section *Pseudoregelia.* This section includes species that are neither stoloniferous nor rhizomatous; new fans are formed close to the base of existing fans, and compact nonrunning clumps are formed in time. Most if not all species have few, thick, more-or-less fleshy storage roots, and finer hairy feeder roots. The seeds are arillate, and only the falls are bearded. Some species bear flowers that are notably streaked, mottled, and spotted, such as *I. tigridia* and *I. kemaonensis.* The section name implies a relationship with the true regelia (section *Regelia*) irises. I defer to the designations of B. Mathew in regard to the closely related regelia and hexapogon iris. Other authors include both sections *Psammiris* and *Pseudoregelia* together with the sections *Regelia* and *Hexapogon,* and any of these names have been used to include all the Chinese species as well as those from other locations. My selection of species for inclusion is based on seeing living materials where fresh fleshy roots are very obvious and stolons are also more readily observed.

Section *Psammiris* is typified by the Chinese species *I. flavissima.* There has been considerable debate over the identification and true name of this species and its relationship to the named species *I. arenaria, I. humilis* and *I. stolonifera.* I have used the designation provided by Zhao and neither deny nor confirm the distinctiveness or similarity of any of these species. *I. flavissima* has a distribution in China that is nearly 4000 km (2500 mi) across the northern tier of provinces, and its affinities seem to be to the north and west. Specimens from this wide, north Chinese range are exceedingly few. There is considerable possibility that major gaps occur in this distribution from east to west, and major differences in plants may occur from east to west. The distribution of the *arenaria-humilis* complex is in eastern Europe almost another 4000 km (2500 mi) from the extreme western border of China. I would assume that over a range of more than 8000 km (5000 mi), there may be not only considerable variation, but more likely geographic isolation conducive to speciation. Extensive field study is needed to determine the specific distribution of this species or species complex. Plants that I observed in Jilin Province are near the extreme eastern portion of the range of this species. Living plants that I brought to the United States may be the first living material of this species introduced into cultivation from the eastern edge of its range. Plants of this material are much larger in all respects than plants I have seen designated as *arenaria-humilis*. The true *Iris stolonifera* is unrelated to any psammiris and is not found in China.

Iris bloudowii and *I. curvifolia* are not known to me, but information in the literature seems to justify inclusion in the section Psammiris. These species are found in dry grasslands or sandy soils of dunes. This section is commonly known as sand iris for its affinity with sandy locations with good drainage.

Section *Pseudoregelia* makes up most of the bearded species in China. They range in size from the small *I. tigridia* and *I. potaninii*, which reach only to about 10 cm (4 in), up to *I. leptophylla* which grows to over 38 cm (15 in) in height. They all tend to be plants of higher elevations, and some are found at extremely high altitude— over 4000 m (13,000 ft) in *I. goniocarpa, I. kemaonensis,* and *I. dolichosiphon*. These are also not well known to science or in cultivation, and some species have been confused with both the sections *Psammiris* and *Regelia*.

Iris mandshurica seems to belong in this section. It has all the distinctive characteristics indicated above for the section *Pseudoregelia* and none for the section *Psammiris*. This is the first time *I. mandshurica* has been suggested to be a pseudoregelia iris. The species *I. leptophylla* has been known since 1922, but was not brought into cultivation until recently. The similar *I. sichuanensis* was described in 1980. There is enough similarity in herbarium material to suggest these two are closely related. *I. sichuanensis* is a larger plant in all aspects and may be a geographic form of *I. leptophylla* and more properly designated as *I. leptophylla sichuanensis*.

Both species have a curious, short, globe-shaped, tuberlike rhizome. This structure appears to be a storage organ, but its function is not clear. It does not appear to be either a true rhizome or stolon. These species form compact clumps of fans typical of other pseudoregelias.

Iris narcissiflora remains a mystery in this section. It was first described from a single collection in southwest Sichuan in 1924. The few herbarium specimens consist only of flowering stems without any vegetative structures such as roots, rhizome, or even leaves. It was known until recently from only a single location in Sichuan, but has since been collected in locations as widespread as Luding, Woolong, and Shimian, all in west central Sichuan. All these locations are above 2000 m (6500 ft) in elevation. It has yet to be introduced into cultivation, and its true affinities remain unclear. In any case, it is obviously a distinct species and probably belongs in this section.

The poorly known species *Iris pandurata* appears, from the skimpy literature descriptions, to belong in this section. The newly described *Iris dolichosiphon*, a pseudoregelia, is closely allied to *I. kemaonensis*. It differs from that species primarily in the much longer perianth tube of up to 14 cm (5.5 in), the unblotched deep-purple flower color, and the shape of the seed capsule.

Subgenus *Limniris*

Most iris species in China are beardless, which in general are better known than the bearded species. Some mysteries remain, but these are relatively easy to solve based on introduction to horticulture, increased cultivation, and laboratory investigations. Exact distributions of these iris are also extremely poorly known.

The crested or Lophiris make up a section of the genus *Iris* with a unique worldwide distribution. Most species are Chinese, but there is one other Asian representative, the unique *I. gracilipes* in Japan. The other species are found in North America; *I. tenuis* isolated in the Pacific Northwest, *I. lacustris* in a limited area around Lake Michigan, and the more widespread *I. cristata* in the eastern United States. The overall variety in distribution, form, and biology suggests that this may be an unrelated collection of iris species that share a few anatomical characteristics.

The Chinese species are easily divided into subgroups in which some affinities seem clearer. The largest subgroup in China consists of the closely related *I. confusa, I. formosana, I. japonica,* and *I. wattii*. These species have been the cause of considerable confusion, as indicated in part by the name, *I. confusa*. There is also some doubt as to the distinction of each of them. At various times *I. confusa* and *I. wattii* have been mixed up. *I. japonica* and *I. confusa* may be variants of the same species, and *I. formosana* may be an island form of one of these species. Added to the confusion is that although all these species are known in cultivation, it is unclear whether the plants in cultivation correspond to typical wild materials. In cultivation, hybrids are common and misidentified plants of possible hybrid origin are likely.

The two best known species in cultivation, *I. japonica* and *I. confusa*, are most likely the results of atypical plants collected in China, and cultivated in Japan for centuries. Cultivated plants of both species seem self-sterile—neither produce fertile seeds. Yet hybrids between these species are widespread and numerous. Herbarium specimens suggest that there may be both fertile and sterile forms of both species. Furthermore, these two species may simply be variants of just one species. Prof. Yen Chi, director of the Triticae Research Institute, and his wife, Prof. Yang Jun Liang, both of Sichuan Agricultural University, have been collecting and observing these species in the wild. Reports on distribution, karyotypes, and relationships should be forthcoming.

Iris wattii has been introduced only twice from wild collections, one of these from southern Yunnan Province. The two collections are somewhat distinct plants, and neither has been widely distributed. Obviously *I. formosana* is native to Taiwan (Formosa), and it may be a local variant or hybrid involving *I. japonica*. It has not been studied extensively in the wild, and cultivated material is of dubious identity.

Iris tectorum and *I. milesii* form a pair of related species. Both are distinct and widely grown. *Iris milesii* was introduced from India and *I. tectorum* from Japan. The remaining crested species are of unclear relationships, which reflects their absence from cultivation. *I. proantha* has long been incorrectly known as *I. pseudorossii* (a junior synonym), and *I. latistyla* was only described from herbarium material from Tibet in 1980. It has never been cultivated. One can only speculate about the relationships among the Japanese, American, and Chinese species. Judging from the dissimilarities within the crested iris, I suspect that the ties among Chinese, Japanese, and North American species are fairly ancient.

The *Chinenses* series may constitute the most Chinese of all Chinese iris. Their actual distribution in China is poorly known and their taxonomy confused. There are six known species in this series. The least known is *Iris henryi*, a small purple-flowered species with a wide and uneven distribution. Known from few collections in the east, north central, and southwest, it has never been introduced into cultivation. *Iris koreana,* as the name suggests, was described first from Korea, but also occurs in border areas of adjacent Jilin and Liaoning provinces. It is yellow flowered and seems most closely related to the smaller, yellow-flowered *I. minutoaurea,* with a similar distribution. The latter had been known only from cultivated plants grown in Japan for centuries. It is among the smallest flowered of all known iris. *Iris minutoaurea* has been recorded from China and North Korea. The other species in this series, the Korean *I. odaesanensis,* is a white-flowered species restricted to the peak of Mt. Odaesan in Korea. It apparently grows in open grassland, and the thin rhizome runs along near the soil surface. It, too, is not in cultivation. Like *I. minutoaurea,* the small purple-flowered *I. rossii* is known in cultivation only from Japanese horticulture. It occurs in Korea and nearby China.

The last in the series is *Iris speculatrix,* long considered the only tropical iris after it was first described from Hong Kong. Zhao has recently shown that it is identical with *I. grijsi* (a junior synonym), and it has a distribution over a large area of eastern China. Considered by some authorities to be a member of the crested iris group, *I. speculatrix* seems more closely allied to the series *Chinenses.* Like the other species in this series, it has evergreen foliage and thin rhizomes, and it tends to form clumps. The crested species tend to be deciduous, have curious thick and thin rhizomes, and spread rapidly to form open clumps or more widely spaced separate fans. The presence of a crest on the falls, typical of the crested irises, has not been accurately determined in *Iris speculatrix.* There is a raised or thickened but inconspicuous ridge on the center of each fall. This ridge and the striking, highly contrasting color pattern make the "crest" areas dominate the flower in *I. speculatrix.* This raised area differs, however, from the comblike crest of the other crested iris species. Careful observation of this iris in cultivation and and hybridization trials may shed more light on its relationships to other species in the genus.

Although plants of this series are almost unknown in the wild, the few cultivated plants share some characteristics. They all have thin rhizomes and fans in close clumps. The leaves are fairly thick and dark, and tend toward being evergreen. Some show strong ribs and veins and may appear to have pleated leaves. All seem to be reasonably hardy plants of open environments.

The *Ruthenicae* series consists of two or possibly three species. *Iris caespitosa* is found in the USSR and is of doubtful validity. The two remaining species are quite similar, but can easily be distinguished in bloom. *Iris uniflora* has thick resilient bracts beneath the single flower, while *I. ruthenica* has soft flexible bracts. Squeezing the bracts between thumb and forefinger is enough to determine identity; *I. ruthenica* will flatten when squeezed; *I. uniflora* will bounce back. Both species seem to be quite variable in the wild, with white-flowered, pale-colored, and various shades of blue to reddish purple blooms. *I. ruthenica* also has forms with short flower stems as well as long. Both are found in open grassland in northern areas.

Iris setosa is the only member of its series (*Tripetalae*) in China. This is the only species found in both the eastern and western hemispheres. It is restricted to high elevations in the Changbai Mountains of Jilin Province near the North Korean border. The Chinese form has not been given any variant name. This species is fairly easy to identify from the extremely reduced standards. In some forms they may be up to 2.5 cm (1 in) or slightly more in length, in others reduced to mere spikes, and in some totally absent. There are also dwarf forms. Hybridization with the Siberian irises suggests some affinity.

Siberian irises (series *Sibiricae*) are perhaps the most widely grown of all Chinese species. All but one species are found in China, and therefore the Siberian irises are the best-known Chinese irises. The species can clearly be divided into two groups based on chromosome numbers. The Sino-Siberian or 40-chromosome species are restricted to southwest China, essentially Sichuan, Yunnan, and Tibet provinces. Mysteries abound in this group, such as *Iris bulleyana*, which was of uncertain origins. Recently Professor Zhao confirmed its wild distribution and determined its validity. *Iris dykesii* is another species in this group that has an uneven history. This iris was found growing in the garden of W. R. Dykes, after his death, along with some seedlings from Chinese collected seeds, but its specific wild origin remains unknown. The species in this group cross freely and produce numerous fertile hybrids.

This 40-chromosome group of Sino-Siberian irises has some affinity to the American *Californicae* (Pacific Coast irises) series. All of the latter 11 species have 40 chromosomes, and numerous garden hybrids have been produced between these groups. The Cal-Sibe hybrids are intermediate between the two groups and are sterile.

Members of the second group, known as "garden Siberians," have 28 chromosomes. This group was composed until recently of only two known species: *I. sibirica,* which is not native to China; and *I. sanguinea,* which is found in northeastern China. Two other species have been somewhat elusive. *Iris typhifolia* was described in 1934, but only recently have new collections been made and the species brought into cultivation. This species has very narrow slightly twisted leaves like the unrelated *Typha,* the cattail, and should prove very hardy. Perhaps it can be crossed with existing species and hybrids in this series. The remaining Chinese 28-chromosome Siberian iris has proved the most problematic: *I. phragmitetorum.* No further specimens have been located since the single collection in northwest Yunnan in 1925. It appears somewhat similar to *I. sanguinea* although quite distant in distribution. Until more material is collected, the affinities of this iris remain unknown. Although it is closest in distribution to the Sino-Siberians, this species may be the most southerly of the 28-chromosome group if the physical similarities prove true. This should be one of the more sought-after irises to be located in China because of its rarity, deep blue color, and southerly distribution.

Chinese water irises (series *Laevigatae*) include some horticultural favorites: the Japanese Iris (*I. ensata*) and *I. laevigata.* The common European Yellow Water Iris (*I. pseudacorus*) is not native to China; however, a curious parallel exists with the little-known *I. maackii.* This latter iris is the only other yellow-flowered member of this series and grows along the Wusuli (Ussuri) River border between Russia and Heilongjiang Province of northeast China. Descriptions indicate it is very similar to the European species, but smaller in all aspects. It has not been introduced into cultivation. There are numerous hybrids between members of this group, but not beyond.

The only spuria iris (series *Spuriae*) in China is *I. halophila.* With its extremely northern distribution, it is clearly at the edge of its large range. Its affinities lie to the north and east in the USSR and Europe.

The *Tenuifoliae* series is another unique group within the genus. All species are found in China with the exception of *I. regelii,* a little-known Russian species which seems close to *I. tenuifolia.* This odd group probably consists of two or more subgroups. *Iris bungei* and *I. ventricosa* both possess inflated bracts beneath the flowers and are probably closely related to each other. *Iris tenuifolia* and *I. loczyi* (and its synonym *I. tianshanica*) are also similar; both have thin threadlike leaves, although those of *I. tenuifolia* are more so. Most of the species in this group are too poorly known to determine specific relationships. There is a group of generally small, narrow-leaved species which may include the scattered *I. cathayensis*, *I. kobayashi*, and *I. qinghainica*. In addition are *Iris songarica*, a widespread species that may be related to *I. ventricosa*, and two related rare species, *I. farreri* and *I. polysticta*. The latter have been collected infrequently, and some authorities have linked them to the series *Spuriae* irises. This seems unlikely; I include them in the *Tenuifoliae* in deference to Zhao's placement there. Much study and field work is needed to understand the definition of these species and even more to explain the relationships in this large series of irises.

Iris lactea is the sole member of the series *Ensatae* and is widely distributed throughout China, Russia, and many neighboring countries. Although quite distinct, it may have affinities to the series *Tenuifoliae*. It has been known under a wide range of incorrect names, most notably *I. ensata*, *I. biglumis*, *I. iliensis*, *I. oxypetala*, *I. moorcroftiana*, and probably numerous others. This confusion in nomenclature is odd because this iris is easily distinguished from all others by the foliage and clump form alone. Once seen, it is not easily confused with other species.

Iris anguifuga is a distinct species placed by Zhao in its own section (*Ophioiris*). Long known and grown in China for its herbal and alleged medicinal qualities, it is a very odd iris. It is the only species with a single bract below each flower. The rhizome is quite different also, and the habit of summer dormancy is unusual in its environment. Mathew has suggested an affinity to the series *Tenuifoliae*, but I doubt this relationship and believe that *Iris anguifuga* warrants a distinct treatment within the genus. The rhizome and foliage are unlike any other iris I know. The rhizome is thick and rounded, reddish brown, and nearly woody covered in a fine net of hairs. When dormant, the live buds are very small and not obvious. I have not seen a living flower, but the line drawing resembles the very different *I. foetidissima* or a spuria iris variant. Some spurias tend to go at least partially dormant in hot dry summers.

Subgenus *Nepalensis*

This is a distinct subgenus, long separated from the rest of the genus because of the unusual structure of its tuberous roots. Usually the roots are compared to those of the unrelated Liliaceae genus *Hemerocallis*. The roots are obviously the main storage organ as there is little or no hint of a rhizome or bulb. *Iris decora* is well known and widely cultivated, while the related *I. collettii* remains uncultivated. The relationship of these two species to others in the genus seems distant.

Genus *Pardanthopsis*

Although Zhao considers *Paranthopsis* a subgenus of the genus *Iris,* most authorities now view it as a separate and distinct genus. Lee Lenz has given substantial evidence for its separation as a distinct genus. The single species *P. dichotoma* is well known in cultivation although it appears in few wild Chinese collections. The newly described *P. subdichotoma* seems to be misplaced in this genus. Until more material is made available for study, its affinity remains unclear. I suspect it may be closer to the crested irises, and I have placed it there very tentatively.

Pardanthopsis dichotoma is obviously related to another genus in the Iridaceae, *Belamcanda,* as there are now numerous reports of fertile hybrids between *P. dichotoma* and *B. chinensis.* These form a series of garden hybrids known as × *Pardancanda norrisii.* I know of no hybrids of *P. dichotoma* with members of the genus *Iris.*

A number of species are poorly known or virtually unknown in the West. My discussions with scientists in China suggest that there are more to be described; as few as five or six or perhaps as many as 20 new iris species still await definition. Untouched by field research, vast areas of China retain floral secrets. The problem is twofold: China has suffered from a shortage of trained field scientists, while foreign collectors have been uneven in their targets, timing, and geographic coverage.

Recent works by Zhao and others are bringing new light to the Chinese *Iris* flora and to the relationships between old, well-known species and newly described species. The following table includes the best approximation of these relationships for all of the known native and introduced species. The introduced species are marked *. Subspecies, forms, and varieties are not included. Following each species name is a number in parentheses, indicating the diploid chromosome (2n) number, although the data are far from complete. Few of the counts given are for actual materials of Chinese origin. Thanks to Dr. Norlan Henderson and the American Iris Society for assistance in compiling this information.

Genus *Iris* L.
  1. Subgenus *Iris* L.
    A. Section *Iris* L.
      I. × *germanica* L. * (44, 48)
      I. pallida Lam. * (24)
      I. scariosa Willd. ex Link. (24)
    B. Section *Psammiris* (Spach) J. Taylor
      I. bloudowii Ledeb. (16, 22, 26)
      I. curvifolia Y. T. Zhao
      I. flavissima Pall. (22)
    C. Section *Pseudoregelia* Dykes
      I. dolichosiphon Noltie (22)
      I. goniocarpa Baker
      I. kemaonensis D. Don ex Royle (22)
      I. leptophylla Lingelsheim
      I. mandshurica Maxim. (34, 40)
      I. narcissiflora Diels
      I. pandurata Maxim.
      I. potaninii Maxim. (22)
      I. sichuanensis Y.T. Zhao
      I. tigridia Bunge (38)
  2. Subgenus *Limniris* Spach
    A. Section *Lophiris* Spach
      I. confusa Sealy (30)
      I. formosana Ohwi (28, 35)
      I. japonica Thunb. (34, 36, 54)
      I. latistyla Y. T. Zhao
      I. milesii Baker ex M. Foster (26)
      I. proantha Diels (44)
      I. tectorum Maxim. (28, 32, 36)
      I. wattii Baker (30)
      I. subdichotoma Y. T. Zhao (tentative)
    B. Section *Limniris* (Tausch) Spach em. Rodion.
      a. Series *Chinenses* (Diels) Lawr.
        I. henryi Baker
        I. koreana Nakai
        I. minutoaurea Makino (22)
        I. rossii Baker (32)
        I. speculatrix Hance (44)
      b. Series *Ruthenicae* (Diels) Lawr.
        I. ruthenica Ker-Gawl. (84)
        I. uniflora Pall. ex Link. (42)

c. Series *Tripetalae* (Diels) Lawr.
    I. setosa Pall. ex Link. (38, 54)
d. Series *Sibiricae* (Diels) Lawr.
    I. bulleyana Dykes (40)
    I. chrysographes Dykes (40)
    I. clarkei Baker (40)
    I. delavayi Mich. (40)
    I. dykesii Stapf
    I. forrestii Dykes (40)
    I. phragmitetorum Hand.-Mazz.
    I. sanguinea Donn ex Horn. (28)
    I. sibirica L. * (28)
    I. typhifolia Kitagawa (28?)
    I. wilsonii C. H. Wright (40)
e. Series *Laevigatae* (Diels) Lawr.
    I. ensata Thunb. (24)
    I. laevigata Fisch. (32, 34)
    I. maackii Maxim.
    I. pseudacorus L.* (32, 34)
    I. versicolor L.* (108)
f. Series *Spuriae* (Diels) Lawr.
    I. halophila Pall. (44)
g. Series *Tenuifoliae* (Diels) Lawr.
    I. bungei Maxim.
    I. cathayensis Migo
    I. farreri Dykes
    I. kobayashi Kitagawa
    I. loczyi Kanitz
    I. polysticta Diels
    I. qinghainica Y. T. Zhao
    I. songarica Schrenk
    I. tenuifolia Pall. (28)
    I. ventricosa Pall.
h. Series *Ensatae* (Diels) Lawr.
    I. lactea Pall. (40, 44)
C. Section *Ophioiris* Y. T. Zhao
    I. anguifuga Y. T. Zhao (34)
3. Subgenus *Nepalensis* (Dykes) Lawr.
    I. collettii Hook. f. (28, 30, 40)
    I. decora Wall. (28, 30, 36)

Genus *Pardanthopsis* (Hance) Baker
    P. dichotoma Pall. (32, 36)

2. From China to Our Gardens

Chinese iris have been known to science since 1776 when *Iris lactea* was first described, but from Russian, not Chinese materials. The first Chinese species to be described was *Iris japonica*, but this too was described from Japan, probably from material originating in China. The first truly native Chinese iris—*Iris maackii*—was described to the West in 1880. By an odd coincidence that species is still all but unknown. A strange combination of events has led to the odd fact that although many species of *Iris* native to China are known in cultivation, very few Chinese irises have been introduced into cultivation from plants collected in China.

Perhaps the most widely grown of all Chinese irises is *Iris tectorum*, yet it is commonly known as the "Japanese Roof Iris." This species was probably introduced to Japan from China centuries ago. First described and introduced from Japan, this iris has been associated with Japan ever since. The most Chinese of Chinese irises in cultivation are the 40-chromosome Sino-Siberian irises, gathered incidental to the rhododendron and other woody plant collections of the Victorian era. Starting in 1892 all the Sino-Siberian species were described and named within 20 years except for the more recent and still problematic *Iris dykesii*.

Some of the world's great garden irises are native to China, but little actual Chinese material has contributed to cultivation in the West. Widely grown irises in the Japanese and garden Siberian groups as well as *I. japonica, I. confusa, I. tectorum, I. laevigata, I. lactea,* and *I. ruthenica* originate from non-Chinese sources. Extremely few irises in cultivation are from verified Chinese collections. Except for the Sino-Siberians, there would be practically none.

Professor Zhao's publication of the genus *Iris* in *Flora Reipublicae Popularis Sinica* (see Part II) and the conclusion of the Cultural Revolution increased Western knowledge and understanding of China's great iris flora. New collections of iris are being made both by Chinese field scientists and Western visitors. These collections of herbarium material, seeds, and living plants are making their way to herbaria, botanical gardens, arboreta, and individual gardeners in the West. As living materials are brought to the West, we will learn how to cultivate, propagate, and distribute them. Some may be excellent additions to the garden palette while others will remain difficult or oddities of scientific or collectors' interest only.

My travels to China in spring of 1989 and subsequent exchanges of seeds and plants were the first and largest concentrated effort to introduce Chinese irises into Western cultivation. Seventeen species of living plants were distributed to gardens in the United States, Canada, and France. Seeds and plants of additional species have had wider distribution through the Species Iris Group of North America seed exchange program.

Some noteworthy new introductions from China have already suggested a high potential for additions to our gardens. The most widely grown of the beardless species groups are probably the Siberian irises. Until now the garden hybrids have been based on only the two 28-chromosome species, *I. sibirica* and *I. sanguinea*. With the addition of a third species, *Iris typhifolia*, we may soon have a major new contribution to the gene pool. This species was first brought to flower in the West in England in late 1989. Even without flowers, other characteristics are worth noting. The foliage is quite thin and slightly twisted for an elegant foliage effect. This is the most northerly of Chinese Siberian irises, and its hardiness may add to the northern range of iris growing. The flowers are blue-purple, and there are no known variations in color, form, or stature. Since *I. typhifolia* has a possibly large distribution along the Amur River, as more material of other collections is introduced, we may see more variety introduced later.

Seeds and seedlings have been distributed to hybridizers in the United States, England, France, and Germany. Within the next few years garden hybridizers will make crosses with modern hybrids. Perhaps we will have an entirely new race of Mongolian iris hybrids that will come in a range of colors, have graceful foliage, and be hardy throughout North America and across northern Europe.

On the southern end of this spectrum is the yet-to-be introduced *Iris phragmitetorum*. This species is also thought to be a 28-chromosome Siberian iris. It may be more heat tolerant than the other Siberian irises. This iris and its hybrids may contribute Siberian iris that can be grown in southern locations in the United States and southern Europe.

Another small group of iris species that contains some widely grown species and cultivars is the series *Laevigatae* or water irises.

Cultivars of *Iris ensata, I. laevigata,* and *I. pseudacorus* grace gardens around the world. *Iris maackii,* which has not yet been introduced, offers another new element to water gardens. This iris is a large-flowered yellow iris allied to *I. pseudacorus.* From the descriptions, it appears to be quite similar to the latter, but the vegetative parts are modest and more suited to small gardens and ponds. It has potential for crossing with both *I. laevigata* and *I. ensata* to produce yellow-flowered hybrids in those lines. Attempts to hybridize the latter species with the European *I. pseudacorus* have proven frustrating at best. Although the chromosome number or compatibility remains unknown, this is at the least the only yellow-flowered Asian water iris.

For the rock gardener, Chinese iris have barely been tapped. *Iris mandshurica* is a tightly clumping, bright yellow iris perfectly suited to hot dry rock garden situations. This will be a cheery addition to northern gardens. The closely related *Iris tigridia* will not only have the same rock garden value, but also an extra bonus. The striped and mottled color pattern may be of value as it is introduced into the bearded iris gene pool. There are a number of hybrids among the sections *Regelia, Oncocyclus,* and *Iris.* Irises of the section *Pseudoregelia* generally have not been used, but they have also not been available for hybridizers. *Iris tigridia* makes impressive clumps, and some color variations have been noted in the wild from blues through purples.

Special note needs to be made of *Iris sichuanensis* since it has the largest flowers of this section. From a short distance, the size and color of the flower is reminiscent of the unrelated *I. tectorum.* In the wild it exhibits a variety of shades of color from purple to reddish purple. Whether this species can be hybridized with the other bearded iris remains to be seen.

For the woodland garden, *Iris speculatrix* and *I. proantha* remain challenges of sorts. The exact growing conditions of *Iris speculatrix* are not yet clear. It may be suited to high bright shade as well as to open exposed locations. On the other hand, *Iris proantha* is definitely a woodland plant. Both species are small but charming and have definite appeal for the temperate woodland garden.

Iris anguifuga is certainly an iris for collectors. I have not seen this in flower, but drawings of the flower make it appear less than spectacular. It appears easy to grow, however, and may be suited to some climates more than others. It belongs to a distinct division within the genus, and offers the adventurous hybridizer new material for totally new possibilities. I am intrigued by the thought of crossing a summer deciduous iris with an evergreen iris such as

I. foetidissima. Drawings of the flowers have a passing similarity both to *I. foetidissima* and the smaller spuria irises. The newly introduced plants are slowly becoming established in cultivation and will offer new challenges to species iris growers and hybridizers.

FUTURE PROSPECTS

Almost half of all Chinese native iris species are poorly known in cultivation, and even more are not known from plant materials originating from Chinese native sources. Fortunately, recent introductions from various native sources have brought more Chinese materials to the West than ever before. In addition, Chinese scientists are making great progress in initiating and conducting field work to collect new materials for basic research. Field research in China has had many difficulties, including hazards beyond the challenges of travel in remote areas. Encouragement is needed to support the efforts of Chinese and Western scientists to investigate the basics of identification and distribution, and in-depth studies of karyotypes, physiology, and genetics. In coming years there will be even more Chinese material of more Chinese species than in the past 100 years.

Still more intriguing for the long term is the prospect that everyone will benefit as China becomes more aware of its native iris species and as living material of these iris comes into Western gardens. Chinese iris researchers will undoubtedly discover new species as well as unravel the continuing mysteries of distribution, biology, and systematics. Western gardeners will have new opportunities for horticulture and hybridizing. With the increased interest in wide species crosses—hybrids between species of different sections and series within the genus—new Chinese introductions may provide the basis for a wider range of garden irises than now exists.

I believe it is essential that Western and Chinese gardeners and scientists cooperate to bring these new discoveries to light and make new material known and available around the world. Traditional methods of propagation have led to advances in tissue culture, for example, and this new technology may be needed to propagate new iris finds quickly and in large enough numbers to introduce them widely to gardens.

This book is part of that effort to introduce Chinese irises to the West, but it is only a small part of all that has gone before and an even smaller preview of what may come ahead. Prof. Zhao Yu-tang will be represented in the official English edition of the *Flora of*

China. He has begun work on a popular book on Chinese irises, and he continues to contribute scientific articles to both Western and Chinese journals. Other Chinese scholars and students have begun to write in Chinese journals about their iris flora. In addition to increased Chinese research and scholarship, sporadic articles in Western journals have described collections and observations in China that have included irises. More has been written on Chinese irises based on real experiences in China in the past 10 years than in the previous 80 years.

Historically China has kept its doors closed to Western ideas and materials. The Cultural Revolution caused some severe restructuring in China, set back many studies of long-term scientific interest, and devalued science itself. Yet during recent decades, the prospects for science in China have developed at a greater rate than ever before in this century. Scientists who have disdained field work are now going out across the country observing and collecting data and materials at an ever-increasing rate. Introduction of modern techniques, greater communication with the West, and the encouragement of scientific study will produce comprehensive research on all aspects of the Chinese flora. Surely new discoveries will follow.

A growing pool of reports suggests that some species of Chinese iris may be reaching endangered population levels. Some of the difficulty in introducing iris into cultivation may be due to population growth and expansion of urban areas. *Iris phragmitetorum* was collected in what is now Kunming city, the capital of Yunnan Province. *Iris kobayashi* can no longer be located in known urban sites in Shenyang, Liaoning Province, and *Iris sanguinea yixingensis* is apparently gone from Jiangsu Province, its only known location. While *Iris lactea* expands its range, others are surely receding. To date the Chinese government has been very mindful of its conservation responsibilities, but no iris have been included in official plans. This is due in great part to the lack of concrete information.

As a student and observer of the irises of China, I eagerly anticipate the events and plants that will be coming. China has been known for its great civilization, huge populations, massive construction, and wondrous accomplishments. I am sure the irises to come will be worth the wait and equally enthralling.

3. *Cultivating Chinese Iris*

Chinese irises include some of our old garden favorites. The Siberian and Japanese irises and their hybrids have long been the subject of serious hybridizers, casual gardeners, and landscapers alike, and for good reason. Smaller distinct groups are the target of specialist growers, while a few individual species are also well-loved garden mainstays. Many species are very tolerant of a variety of cultivation methods and amenable to good garden practices. Other species defy our efforts and are challenging in cultivation, and far too many Chinese species have never been introduced into cultivation, as we have seen earlier inn this book.

A few Chinese irises are available from general nursery sources, but rarer species are only obtained from specialist nurseries such as those listed in Appendix 4. The newest introductions will be slow to come into the commercial trade. Avid growers can obtain seed, and sometimes plants, through exchanges sponsored by the specialist organizations such as the Species Iris Group of North America and others.

The following sections correlate the ecology of Chinese iris species as they grow in the wild and expectations in cultivation. Failure to duplicate natural conditions may be one reason why certain species do not survive under traditional cultivation methods. Some species are more demanding of exacting growing conditions than others, and the most demanding will probably never be common garden subjects.

Each plant discussion considers those aspects of each species' environment, anatomy, and lifestyle that may suggest likely horticultural treatment for best results. I will try to suggest cultivation methods even for those not now in cultivation. Because I garden in Kansas City, Missouri, near the borders of USDA Zones 5 and 6, I am influenced by cold, continental, temperate conditions. My garden is subject to cold winters and hot summers. Late spring frosts are my biggest dilemma. Please bear in mind your specific growing conditions when considering my suggestions.

In the guide that follows, each section concludes with "Cultivation Basics," an assessment of the ease or difficulty of growing these species and a summary of essential information including:

SOIL
> *Average*   A wide range of soils is suitable and there are no special needs.
>
> *Acid*   Special care should be used to ensure that acidic (under pH 6.5) soil conditions are maintained.

WATER
> *Average*   The plant tolerates a typical temperate schedule of rainfall: spring rains, summer drying, and winter precipitation.
>
> *Wet*   The plant needs very damp soils and should not be allowed to dry out. Standing water may not be tolerated, however.
>
> *Moist*   The plant should be kept moist and should never be allowed to dry out.
>
> *Dry*   The plant requires extra drainage to ensure that the rhizome is kept on the dry side. Spring moisture is usually needed, but dry summer and winter conditions are also preferred.

EXPOSURE
> *Sun*   The plant requires full sun, a minimum of six hours per day in the growing season.
>
> *Shade*   The plant requires shady, generally woodland conditions. Full sun should be avoided especially in climates with hot intense summer sun.

HARDINESS
> I will suggest USDA Hardiness Zones. The current map of China Hardiness Zones appears as Appendix 4; that of the U.S. appears as Appendix 5.

SPECIAL NEEDS
> Notes in this section will clarify the special requirements of some species, such as cold and drought tolerance and tips on success in various climates.

AVAILABILITY
> *Common*   Species or cultivars available from numerous nursery sources.
>
> *Available*   **Species or cultivars available only occasionally or from specialist nurseries.**
>
> *Uncommon*   Species infrequently available except as seed from specialist growers.
>
> *Rare*   Species rarely or not available.

SIBERIAN IRISES: SINO-SIBERIAN SPECIES

The Sino-Siberian or 40-chromosome Siberians can present a challenge to some gardeners. These are basically plants of high altitudes and near tropics. They are accustomed to neither excessively high nor excessively low temperatures, and they prefer cool, humid conditions. These irises grow in climates that provide cool summers, mild winters, ample rainfall, and high humidity. They will not do well in the extremes of hot continental climates, although once established they can tolerate a wider variety of conditions. Hot summer sun can bake these irises to death. In areas with hot, sunny summers, these irises may bloom better, live longer, and survive longer in light to half shade all year.

In optimum climates they may be grown in nearly full to complete sun. In climates that are hot, they must be given some shade, preferably that provided by high trees. I have seen them growing in China near trees and shrubs which can provide shade for part of each day. Their native provinces of Sichuan and Yunnan are the foggiest areas of China and have the lowest amount of sunlight per year. These plants also appreciate moist to damp soil conditions, so they can be grown in association with water. Soil conditions are not crucial but alkaline sites are to be avoided. Under good conditions the Sino-Siberian irises can be vigorous growers and require regular feeding both in spring and early fall. Care should be taken in planting these near other too-vigorous plants, such as the 28-chromosome Siberians which in equal situations will overpower and outgrow these generally smaller, somewhat more delicate species.

These irises are propagated either by seed, with or without cold stratification before germination, or by division of established clumps in fall. Divisions should consist of multiple fans when possible and should never be allowed to dry out. If drying is a possibility, divisions can be soaked in a bucket of water overnight or even a couple of days without harm to the plants. Seedlings sown early in spring may bloom in their second year, but most will produce flowers by the third growing season. Of course named hybrids and specific cultivars can only be propagated by division of named plants.

The 40-chromosome species hybridize easily with each other. In gardens with mixed collections, bee-crossed hybrids occur frequently and may be vigorous enough to outgrow true species. Today the validity of some species is in doubt because of this hybrid contamination. Hybrids show a variety of form and color.

Many of the species have also been crossed with some of the Pacific Coast irises (series *Californicae*) which also all have 40 chromosomes. These Cal-Sibe hybrids may prove to be hardier plants with the floral virtues of the Pacific Coast Natives. Although these Cal-Sibe hybrids have proven sterile, colchicine-induced tetraploids have fertile pollen. This group may yet produce plants suited to a wider variety of climates than the species and varieties of pure Sino-Siberians or Pacific Coast irises.

Sino-Siberians

Cultivation Basics: Easy in the right climate, otherwise challenging.

SOIL Average to acid, although they do best with added humus and a light organic mulch.

WATER Wet, moist, or average.

EXPOSURE Sun to shade, depending on intensity of sun.

HARDINESS Zones 3 to 7, depending on temperature extremes.

SPECIAL NEEDS The right climate will ensure success. Otherwise overall cool temperatures and high humidity are needed. These can be easy garden subjects in the right climate, difficult to even keep alive in the wrong climate.

AVAILABILITY Common to Available, although pure species are Rare. Numerous cultivars also available.

SIBERIAN IRISES: GARDEN SIBERIANS

The 28-chromosome Siberians are both hardier and more tolerant of environmental extremes than their 40-chromosome counterparts. Although *I. sibirica* and *I. sanguinea* are little grown, there are some named wild selections of both. Many so-called garden Siberian hybrids are primarily selections of the highly variable *I. sibirica*. *Iris sanguinea* until recently has been relatively little used in the development of modern garden hybrids.

The newly introduced *I. typhifolia* is native to extreme northeast China; *I. sanguinea* comes from even farther north in Siberian Asia. Both are usually associated with water and found at the edges of swamps and marshes. Once established, they can tolerate a typical temperate rainfall cycle if the soil is not allowed to dry totally. These species usually grow in the open but can tolerate light shade.

Once established, plants of these species can be grown in the garden for years without dividing. Large established clumps profit from regular spring feeding. Propagation is by seed or division. Although it is generally advised to divide in fall, they can be divided with care during any season. Divisions should contain multiple fans and never be allowed to dry out. Named garden cultivars can only be propagated by divisions; species come true from seed, and many will bloom their second season. Seed from named cultivars cannot be considered the same as the named parent.

Garden Siberians

Cultivation Basics: Among the easiest in most climates, but best in middle to north latitudes.
SOIL Average.
WATER Average to moist.
EXPOSURE Sun preferred or light shade.
HARDINESS Zones 3 to 8 and perhaps beyond. Very tolerant of climatic extremes.
SPECIAL NEEDS None.
AVAILABILITY Common with numerous cultivars except *Iris typhifolia* which is Uncommon.

SIBERIAN IRIS: *IRIS PHRAGMITETORUM*

Although this Siberian iris is now unknown in cultivation, I would not be surprised to see new collections in the coming years. On the other hand, it may no longer exist as more than 60 years have passed since it was first observed. As one of the most southerly of all Siberians, it may also prove more tender than any other Siberian species. It was originally observed growing in a *Phragmites* swamp in Yunnan Province; this suggests that it prefers very moist to wet conditions and full sun. The form of the plant from the only existing herbarium specimen suggests it may be in the 28-chromosome group and thus should grow well in average garden conditions as well as at the waterside in milder climates. Without reconfirmation of its existence, this species remains somewhat speculative. Hopefully our Chinese counterparts will collect *Iris phragmitetorum* and make living materials available to the West.

SERIES *LAEVIGATAE*—WATER IRIS: *IRIS ENSATA*

This species has been cultivated in Japan for so long that it is widely and commonly known as the Japanese iris. Cultivars number in the thousands in Japan, Europe, the United States, and elsewhere. These cultivars are all selections from this single species and in all probability from a limited pool of Japanese origin. I suspect that there has been little or no recent input from wild Chinese material. It is historically too late to determine the natural extent of this species' range in China and Japan or to place its origin in any specific location.

These iris are in most instances associated with water, but cannot be grown in standing water the year round. Normally, plants are flooded in the spring (either naturally by spring rains or artificially in cultivation) but allowed better drainage later in the year. They are sometimes planted with their crown above water level, either at waterside or in specially prepared raised beds on islands. These iris also require an acidic soil and will suffer and decline in neutral, alkaline, or lime soils. They are exceptionally hardy and tolerant plants.

Work done by Max Steiger in Germany in the 1950s was aimed at developing alkaline-tolerant cultivars. Apparently thousands of seedlings were grown in alkaline soil and surviving seedlings selected and crossed. Unfortunately his work was never completed and none of his crosses are available today. A wealth of information on these irises appears in *The Japanese Iris* (C. McEwen 1990).

These irises are among the easiest to grow from seed, and seed from good-quality plants will produce a wide range of lovely

---

Iris ensata

Cultivation Basics: Fairly easy but with some considerations.

SOIL These require acid soils and prefer high humus content. They benefit from organic mulch and frequent fertilization.

WATER Wet, even standing water in spring only. Or moist to average in the garden border.

EXPOSURE Full sun; can tolerate light shade.

HARDINESS Zone 4 and south.

SPECIAL NEEDS Acid soil and organic amendments produce better growth and flowering.

AVAILABILITY Common with numerous cultivars. Collected wild forms are occasionally available.

---

seedlings. Many will bloom in their second year. Named cultivars must be propagated by divisions which should consist of at least three or more fans and kept moist at all times. Cultivars will vary in their ease of cultivation, vigor, and other considerations. They all benefit from regular spring fertilization to produce best flowering. Japanese iris frequently exhibit yellow foliage because of too high pH or possible lack of certain nutrients.

SERIES *LAEVIGATAE*—WATER IRIS: *IRIS LAEVIGATA*

Iris laevigata is the true water iris of China. Although *I. laevigata* is sometimes confused with *I. ensata*, the two are easily distinguished. *I. ensata* has narrower upright leaves with a pronounced midrib, while *I. laevigata* has wider, softer leaves that are smooth and without a midrib. *Iris laevigata* prefers more water than any other native Chinese species and is best grown in standing water. In the border it needs lots of extra water all year around and should never be allowed to dry out. For this species to be grown at its best, it should be grown in water; thus I cannot recommend it for the border or garden otherwise. I consider it the finest water iris, among the finest of all iris, and worth the trouble of constructing a small pond or boggy area just for this species and its cultivars.

Although it requires abundant water, it is not particular in regard to soil or pH. It is extremely hardy and grows vigorously in standing water. There are relatively few cultivars, but most are quite distinct. An elegant review of this species and its cultivars has been published by the foremost authority, Akira Horinaka (1990) in Japan. I know of no Chinese cultivars and the native Chinese materials are not grown outside of China at this time to the best of my knowledge. In northeast China *I. laevigata* forms large colonies in swamps and may be the dominant vegetation in some areas.

Iris laevigata

Cultivation Basics: Easy in water.

SOIL Average.

WATER Best grown in standing water less than 7 to 10 cm (3 to 4 in) deep. Not suited to the border as it requires copious additional watering all year.

EXPOSURE Sun.

HARDINESS From Zone 3, south.

SPECIAL NEEDS Standing water.

AVAILABILITY Common with cultivars available.

SERIES *LAEVIGATAE*—WATER IRIS: *IRIS MAACKII*

This species has not been introduced into cultivation, but has been collected on the banks and in the swamps surrounding the mouth of the Iman River where it enters the Wusuli (Ussuri) River. It probably occurs in swamps throughout the region. (In Heilongjiang, the most northeasterly province in China, the extreme eastern Chinese border with the USSR is formed in part by the north flowing Wusuli River. The Iman River flows west from Russia. The Wusuli flows in a northeasterly direction and empties into the larger Amur River which continues northwest to empty into the Tatar Straits and eventually into the Sea of Okhotsk.) There are hundreds of square kilometers of swamps and marshes in this corner of Heilongjiang, and these wetlands continue north in vast areas around the Amur River.

When the species was first described in 1880, the area on both banks of the Wusuli River was considered part of China. Today the east bank is part of the Soviet Union. Recent search for this iris along the Chinese border area failed to locate any evidence of this species. The possibility remains that this is not a valid species, but further study is needed to determine its existence.

When or if this species is introduced into cultivation, it will probably prove to be easy to cultivate because of its apparent affinities to the similar and very easy *I. pseudacorus*. It is obviously a water iris, and should prove exceptionally hardy, suited to Zone 3 and perhaps even Zone 2. Like other water iris, it should be vigorous and easy to propagate by seed or division. Cultivation should be similar to *Iris laevigata* or *I. pseudacorus*. It is yellow flowered and about half the stature of the European *I. pseudacorus*. As the only yellow-flowered Asian water iris, it suggests possibilities for new hybrid combinations among these popular species.

SERIES *CHINENSES*

These small irises seem to be plants of open grasslands and forest edges. Hardy and sturdy in their native environment, they have resisted cultivation for various reasons. Because they are all quite small and delicate looking, they are often given protected sites, shade, and extra care. I suspect that these plants of open, exposed areas may actually require somewhat harsher conditions than they are usually given—full sun, summer drought, and no mulch. They tend to be evergreen which may be an adaptation to their small size. That is, they retain their foliage for as long as possible into the winter to continue photosynthesis because their rhizome, the main energy storage organ, is quite thin and small.

Because *I. henryi* and *I. koreana* are not in cultivation, I cannot give specifics, but they occur in fairly cold temperate climates and environments. *Iris rossii* and *I. minutoaurea* are both quite hardy. There are frequent reports of the lack of flowering in both species, but owing to their northern distribution, I suspect they require cold winters for proper bud development. I have grown *I. minutoaurea* in full sun and with full exposure to 37.8° C (100° F), intense summer sun, and −29° C (−20° F) winter cold, unmulched, with good bloom. From an initial planting of three or four fans, in four years I have more than 100 fans. I had the first bloom in the second season after planting and 15 blooms by the third season. The planting has bloomed every year since, but because it is quite small it is not spectacular, and care must be taken to keep it from being overgrown or weeded out.

Iris speculatrix deserves some special commentary. First described from Hong Kong, this species was long considered the most tropical of all true iris species. Occasionally cultivated from plants originating from Hong Kong, these specimens have been short lived and difficult in cultivation. It is now clear that Hong Kong is at the extreme southern edge of the distribution of this plant, and the natural range of the species goes well into regions that experience hard freezes in winter. Its best cultivation seems unclear at this time, although I suspect it can be grown like the unrelated American species, *Iris cristata*, but may not be hardy beyond USDA Zones 6 or 7.

I think it should be grown in nearly full sun, with ample air flow and woodland-edge conditions. Although its actual affinity to the *Chinenses* series is not clear, like them it has evergreen foliage and boldly colored flowers. Plants from the southern part of its range seem to be paler flowered than plants from Zhejiang Province in the north. In Hong Kong this species grows at the highest elevations on open, wind-swept hillsides. It is considered rare and is protected by the Hong Kong government.

These plants must be propagated by division because seed is totally unavailable. *Iris speculatrix* is probably best divided when it is in active growth or in late summer. The two better-known species do not appear to produce viable seed, but this may be due to limited genetic stock and self-infertility. We need more wild collected seed and stocks of this series. The seed pod of *Iris speculatrix* turns at a sharp right angle when ripe and has a sharp point.

Series *Chinenses*

Cultivation Basics: Probably easy, but the difficulty is in obtaining plants. Cultivation will vary from species to species, but some generalities are suggested.

SOIL Average.

WATER Average.

EXPOSURE Sun; *I. speculatrix* and others may tolerate some shade.

HARDINESS Most species will probably be hardy to Zone 5 and further north. *I. speculatrix* probably not hardy beyond Zone 6 or 7.

SPECIAL NEEDS Exposed sites in continental climates and no special delicate treatment.

AVAILABILITY Uncommon to Available, except *I. henryi* and *I. koreana*, which are Rare.

SERIES *TRIPETALAE: IRIS SETOSA*

This species has the distinction of being the only iris found in temperate regions of both the eastern and western hemispheres. *Iris setosa* ranges from the easternmost provinces of Newfoundland and New Brunswick in Canada, to western Canada and Alaska, and across the Bering Straits to the USSR, Japan, and China. There are numerous named geographic variants in this enormous range. *Iris setosa* is also the most northerly of all irises, reported to grow north of the Arctic Circle in climates in which the ground never totally melts in summer. Needless to say, it is very hardy. It prefers soils that are acidic, but can be grown in average garden soils that are never allowed to dry out.

In China the range of this species is restricted to the isolated Changbai Mountains in southeast Jilin Province at the border of North Korea. Here it grows in wet meadows and at the edges of ponds at high altitude. I do not believe that the Chinese form has been given a variety name or introduced into cultivation.

Iris setosa is easily propagated by seed in spring or division in the fall. Several named cultivars including color variants, large-flowered, and dwarf forms are available. Named cultivars, including a beautiful white-flowered Japanese cultivar 'Kosho-En', must be propagated only by division of named stock. *Iris setosa* has been hybridized with some Siberian irises to form a new race of

"Sib-tosa" hybrids. Hybrids have also been made with the Pacific Coast Native irises.

Iris setosa

Cultivation Basics: Easy especially in the north.
SOIL Average to acid.
WATER Average to moist to wet.
EXPOSURE Sun.
HARDINESS At least to Zone 2 and perhaps southern parts of Zone 1. Its heat intolerance may limit it to cooler parts of Zone 6.
SPECIAL NEEDS None; however, this is a species for cold climates.
AVAILABILITY Common with a few cultivars.

SERIES *ENSATAE: IRIS LACTEA*

Iris lactea is the cause of more name confusion than any other Chinese species, but it is certainly one of the easiest to grow. It has been known under a variety of scientific names including the unrelated *I. ensata,* and this has caused some confusion over its cultivation. *Iris lactea* is not a water iris, but a plant of grassland, dry steppe, and uncultivated places in China and across the USSR. It is a common roadside weed in many provinces, and it colonizes abandoned fields and pastures. As a roadside weed it is often covered in dust, but still manages to bloom and set seed. It can take a lot of punishment and grows in areas of very low rainfall where it will barely reach 10 cm or a few inches in height. The roots are coarse and long, growing deep into the soil. It has been recorded for almost every province in China except for the extreme southern ones. I saw it thriving in the cold dry areas of Manchuria as well as in the moist, foggy mountains of Sichuan. It is not particular as to soil or water, but does require full sun. It is very hardy.

The leaves are distinctive with obvious veins running from base to tip. These veins correspond to very tough fibers that have many uses in production of weavings, crude ropes, lashings, paper, and cloth. Although a common rangeland plant, *Iris lactea* is among the last to be eaten; after the leaves have frozen back in winter, sheep and other stock animals will eat the tough leaves.

Like many rugged weeds, *Iris lactea* responds to good horticulture; with proper fertilization and regular watering, it will reward the gardener with more and larger flowers. Easily propagated from seed in spring, seedlings will take two to three years to reach blooming size. This species can be a bit tricky to divide because of its deep and widespreading root system. These plants are best divided into fairly large divisions in early spring or early fall.

Several color variants have been selected by specialist growers, but no major effort has been made to select for larger flower size. The typical flower color in China is pale purple, but off-white forms are known in the wild, and a form from Tibet is described with yellow flowers. Horticultural varieties include bicolored, white, and various shades of purple to reddish purple. The yellow-flowered form has not yet been introduced into cultivation, and there are no named cultivars to my knowledge.

Iris lactea

Cultivation Basics: Easy.
SOIL Any.
WATER Any conditions except wet.
EXPOSURE Sun.
HARDINESS Zone 3, perhaps farther north.
SPECIAL NEEDS None.
AVAILABILITY Common with a few color variations.

SERIES *TENUIFOLIAE*

Although this is a large series of irises, they are generally little known, and few are cultivated. They seem to share some characteristics that may suggest cultivation. They are all plants of dry grassland or semidesert. They all grow in the far north and/or at high altitudes above 2000 m (6500 ft). They are all narrow leaved. Many, perhaps all, have their crowns deep below the soil surface from 2.5 to 10 cm (1 to 4 in). These anatomical features suggest adaptations to prevent water loss, to escape from the cold, and generally to cope with extremely harsh, dry environments. In Jilin and Inner Mongolia, *I. tenuifolia* and *I. ventricosa* grow in very compacted, dry loess soils with their crown totally hidden underground. These areas experience less than 38 cm (15 in) of rainfall per year. During the dry season the soil bakes hard and concrete-like but retains some moisture several centimeters below the surface. *Iris tenuifolia* is also found in highly alkaline and salty soils. These two species are completely deciduous and die back to soil level in winter.

The most widely distributed species, *I. songarica,* is a semidesert and grassland plant that apparently is not in cultivation. It is also the tallest of all the series *Tenuifoliae. Iris kobayashii* and *I. cathayensis* are rare and very small species; neither is cultivated. *Iris bungei* and *I. ventricosa* may be the most amenable to cultivation, but extreme care should be taken in regard to rainfall and drainage. Although these species must be cold and dry in winter, normal seasonal rains occur in their native habitats in May after or about flowering time with little or no additional rainfall at any other time of the year.

Plants should be propagated by seed in spring or when available. Germination may be slow, and it may be delayed for a year or more. Division is difficult because of the deep crowns and brittle, wiry roots. Careful timing and handling are essential for success. These are plants for specialists and require special care.

Series *Tenuifoliae*
Cultivation Basics: Challenging.
SOIL Neutral to alkaline.
WATER Dry to very dry. Care must be taken in watering.
EXPOSURE Sun.
HARDINESS Zones 3 or 4.
SPECIAL NEEDS Many special requirements, but suited to dry, temperate climates.
AVAILABILITY Uncommon to Rare.

SERIES *RUTHENICAE*

This is a small series of two or three dwarf species that is apparently misunderstood horticulturally. *Iris ruthenica* has a large range in Asia and eastern Europe and must tolerate an equally wide range of soils, environments, and climates. *Iris uniflora* is confined to eastern Asia.

Although *I. ruthenica* has been cultivated for years, there appear to be various clones, some of which flower readily, others sparsely. Some have flower stalks that are long and show flowers well above the leaves, while others have shortened flower stems and bloom nearly at ground level. There are also white-flowered and larger-flowered forms.

These are plants of open grassland and harsh northern climates. In Russia they can form large tussocks of grassy leaves after bloom. The leaves are totally deciduous. The plants can be divided when in full growth. The small rhizomes have little food storage and cannot be out of the ground for long. They can also be grown from seed, but seed is rarely available and germination is uneven.

Iris uniflora grows in smaller clumps and is found in open grass in meadows and on hillsides in a much smaller range. In Jilin Province it grows on rocky hillsides at the forest edge. It is subject to cold, dry winters and low rainfall. *Iris caespitosa* has been designated as a third species in this series, but its validity is questionable.

Series *Ruthenicae*

Cultivation Basics: Easy in continental climates.
SOIL Average.
WATER Average to slightly dry.
EXPOSURE Sun.
HARDINESS Zone 3.
SPECIAL NEEDS None, although plants are difficult to obtain and reestablish.
AVAILABILITY Uncommon.

SERIES *SPURIAE: IRIS HALOPHILA*

Iris halophila is an easily cultivated common spuria species. It takes average garden conditions. I do not think the Chinese form is in cultivation. Propagation is by seed or division. Divisions may be slow to reestablish and slow to bloom. It is hardy and undemanding.

Iris halophila

Cultivation Basics: Easy.
SOIL Average.
WATER Average to dry.
EXPOSURE Sun.
HARDINESS Zone 3, possibly Zone 2.
SPECIAL NEEDS None.
AVAILABILITY Available.

SECTION *OPHIOIRIS: IRIS ANGUIFUGA*

Iris anguifuga is an iris unlike any other in China. Although it has been known and grown in China for many years, if not centuries, it was only recently described scientifically and introduced by me to cultivation in the West. Its natural distribution is poorly known because it has been cultivated as a medicinal herb for so long. It has been grown as far north as Anhui and Jiangsu provinces in eastern China. It is a fairly large plant with leaves reaching to more than 60 cm (2 ft) and forming large clumps.

It has a unique lifestyle. The plant is totally dormant in summer with all above-ground growth gone. In late summer to early fall, new growth appears; short, erect leaves remain evergreen all winter. In spring the leaves elongate rapidly, and the plant produces its unique bloom. By mid-May the foliage yellows, wilts, and then disappears. In the Hangzhou Botanical Garden in early May, the coarse foliage was already wilted and yellowing. In my Kansas City garden, the short winter leaves remained evergreen through a winter low near −29° C (−20° F).

Its odd dormancy may have contributed to its supposed medicinal uses and folklore. The species epithet *anguifuga* literally means snake (or eel or worm) and repellant, in reference to its use in traditional Chinese herbal medicine. The rhizome is used directly as a snake repellant, and it is prepared and taken internally as a cure for snake bite. As *Iris anguifuga* resumes active growth in late summer or fall, snakes go into hibernation. There is a belief that the new growth of this iris forces snakes to go into hiding. As snakes hibernate, and enjoy a winter rest, *Iris anguifuga* is above ground and growing. In spring, snakes come out of hibernation, and their renewed vigor corresponds with the late spring to early summer dormancy of the iris. The coincidence of these alter-

---

Iris anguifuga

Cultivation Basics: Unknown but apparently not difficult.

SOIL Average.

WATER Average.

EXPOSURE Sun to light shade.

HARDINESS Unknown, but easily Zone 6.

SPECIAL NEEDS Unknown, but perhaps less water in summer while the plant is dormant.

AVAILABILITY Rare to Uncommon. May become Available.

---

nate lifestyles surely contributed to the belief in a cause-and-effect relationship that could account for practical medicinal qualities of the plant. The plant has been grown in Chinese herb gardens for many years—perhaps centuries—although it has been known to the West for only a few years. I suggest the common name of Snakebane Iris for this species.

The dormant rhizome is easily divided into toes and can be shipped dry or moved at this time. Planted 2 to 5 cm (an inch or two) below the soil, it will begin new growth in fall. Seeds have been unavailable, but may be produced as newly introduced plants prosper, bloom, and set seed.

SECTION *LOPHIRIS:* CRESTED IRISES

This group of species was originally called Evansia irises for the Englishman, Thomas Evans, who introduced *I. japonica* into cultivation. They are also known as the crested irises for the distinct crest in the middle of each fall in most species. Recently the crested irises have been elevated to the section *Lophiris,* and G. I. Rodionenko has raised this group further to the subgenus *Crossiris.* Although each species is distinct, this section very likely has at least two and possibly three or four vaguely related subgroups. I will treat the three Chinese groups that each require cultivation in three different ways.

CRESTED IRISES: *IRIS JAPONICA* GROUP

I. japonica, first described in 1794 and introduced in 1812, is the oldest known Asian crested iris. Although it is named "japonica," I suspect it was introduced into Japan from a source in eastern China. Rodionenko has given this group series status as *Japonicae,* which include the species *I. japonica, I. confusa, I. formosana,* and *I. wattii.* All share some characteristics: they form shiny green fans of evergreen foliage; each forms upright flower stems with multiple flowers; and they all produce underground, thin, wide-running rhizomes. They are all somewhat tender although hardier than widely accepted. Flowering is very early to late winter to early spring; thus, developing flower stems and buds, produced in midwinter, should not be subjected to hard freezes.

For best growth and flowering, the plants should be grown in mild climates and protected from climatic extremes and strong winds. *I. japonica* grows at low altitudes in subtropical regions throughout southern China, while *Iris confusa* and *I. wattii* are more restricted in distribution, and *I. formosana* is confined to the island of Formosa (Taiwan) in nearly tropical conditions. *Iris confusa* is found at higher elevations than *I. japonica* and may be somewhat hardier. It grows both in open situations and under light shade of shrubbery and high trees. In cultivation, there are very few wild collections of these species from known locations in China.

The two best known species in horticulture are *I. japonica* and *I. confusa.* Unfortunately, since they are widely cultivated in China and Japan, their natural distribution has become somewhat obscure. They also hybridize readily with other species in the section so that the material in cultivation may be of hybrid origin. Both in cultivation and in the wild, these species form few seed capsules, and seed is rarely if ever produced. It is widely understood that these species are sterile in cultivation, and it has been suggested that they are triploid, but recent work in China by Prof. Yen Chi suggests more complex genetic interactions. Because of their apparent sterility, the species are generally not grown from seed, and the cultivated material is propagated from the abundantly produced rhizomes.

Iris japonica is a common garden flower in milder parts of China and can been be seen planted along streets in Shanghai. In locations favorable to the species, *I. japonica* and *I. confusa* can be vigorous growers and, because of their wide-roaming underground rhizomes, quite invasive.

Iris japonica group

Cultivation Basics: Easy in mild climates.
SOIL Average.
WATER Average to moist.
EXPOSURE Light shade or full sun in climates without intense sun.
HARDINESS Zone 8 for good flowering of *I. japonica* and *I. confusa*, Zones 9 and 10 for *I. formosana* and *I. wattii*. *Iris japonica* and *I. confusa* will winter over, but not flower regularly, as far north as Zone 6.
SPECIAL NEEDS Shelter from winter winds.
AVAILABILITY Common except for *I. wattii* which is Available.

CRESTED IRISES: *IRIS TECTORUM* GROUP

This group contains the widespread, and well-known, *Iris tectorum* and the less-known *I. milesii*. *Iris tectorum* was introduced to cultivation from Japan, although it was probably of Chinese origin. It is widely distributed and grown in China where it is simply known as "the iris." It is a beautiful iris that grows in a variety of climates and conditions. I have seen it growing in large masses along roadsides as well as isolated on steep hillsides and in city sidewalk landscapes from Zhejiang to Sichuan.

It seems remarkably constant in the wild, although a white-flowered form is cultivated in China and in the West. *Iris milesii* has a much smaller distribution centering in the Himalayas, and it is less widely cultivated. Called the "Red-Flowered Iris," it actually has reddish purple flowers. Although the flowers are very similar to *I. tectorum* in shape, the plant form is very different. The large, solid rhizome, usually bright greenish in color in marked contrast to that of bearded iris, grows just at the soil surface. It has been stated that this iris will not bloom in climates where it is completely deciduous, but that has not been the case in my garden where it dies down totally each winter but blooms reliably each spring. This behavior may be a result of my continental climate.

Both species are easily grown from spring-sown seed and bloom within a couple of years. The few named forms of *I. tectorum* are propagated easily by division of established plants any time during the growing season. There are no named forms of *I. milesii*, but it can also be divided after bloom.

Iris tectorum is the only beardless iris that has produced hybrids with any members of the bearded irises (subgenus *Iris*). There are recorded crosses between *Iris tectorum* and both typical bearded

---

Iris tectorum and *I. milesii*

Cultivation Basics: Easy.
SOIL Average.
WATER Average to moist.
EXPOSURE Sun to light shade.
HARDINESS Zone 5 and perhaps further north for *I. tectorum*.
SPECIAL NEEDS None, although the plants benefit from division and replanting at three or four-year intervals.
AVAILABILITY Common for *I. tectorum*, Available for *I. milesii*.

---

irises as well as arillate species. The only hybrid still in cultivation is 'Pal-Tec', a cross between this species and *Iris pallida*. Oddly there is no record of crosses between *I. tectorum* and *I. milesii*. *Iris tectorum*, highly recommended to any gardener, is a very satisfactory plant for many climates and situations.

CRESTED IRISES: *IRIS PROANTHA*

This is a group of one known member, now called *I. proantha*, but formerly and better known as *I. pseudorossii*. The earlier name derives from the supposed similarity of two poorly known irises, this one and the unrelated *I. rossii* in the series Chinenses. Both are fairly small plants, both have pale lilac flowers, and both have never been widely cultivated. However, they are distinct plants in most of their anatomy.

Iris proantha may have the thinnest rhizome of any member of the genus. I have seen many fresh rhizomes of *I. proantha valida*, the larger form of this species. This rhizome is less than 1.5 mm (1/16 in) in diameter with slightly larger nodes at about 1.2 cm (1/2 in) intervals. Oddly, the fresh new white roots that emerge each spring at the leading edge of the rhizome are about the same diameter as the rhizome, and these grow vigorously as the leaves emerge and the plant blooms.

Out of bloom this plant might never be recognized as an iris; because of the long, narrow, pleated leaves, it can easily be mistaken for a sedge or grass of some kind. Each fan consists of only a few leaves which are open instead of clumped. If growing among other grasslike plants, this species may be overlooked.

The typical form of this species is quite small and delicate, while the less typical larger form, *I. proantha valida*, is larger, but still

---

Iris proantha

Cultivation Basics: Moderate to difficult.
SOIL Average woodland conditions.
WATER Average to moist, probably should not be allowed to dry completely.
EXPOSURE Light shade to half sun.
HARDINESS Probably through Zone 7 and perhaps to Zone 6.
SPECIAL NEEDS Until established in cultivation, its specific needs are unclear.
AVAILABILITY Rare; almost unobtainable.

---

small and delicate. This is a plant of light shade and open woodlands, although it is also reported from grassy areas. Found as far north as Anhui and Jiangsu provinces, it should be hardy through many of the middle parts of the United States. The foliage is totally deciduous in winter. It has only rarely been cultivated and has been very difficult to move due to the very thin and delicate rhizomes. Seed has never been seen and plants are rarely available. When available, *Iris proantha* should be propagated with extreme care, by division when dormant.

SUBGENUS *NEPALENSIS*

Of the two known species, only *I. decora* is in cultivation. *Iris collettii* is a very small species; in flower it tops out to about 5 cm (2 in) according to the account of Brian Mathew. It occurs at high altitudes in southwest China and adjoining parts of Burma, Thailand, and possibly Laos and India. Its distribution beyond that is unknown.

Far more common is *I. decora,* which was long known incorrectly as *I. nepalensis* and which is widespread throughout a large area in the Himalayas from Nepal east to Yunnan and from Burma north to Tibet. *Iris decora* is very delicate in appearance, with thin, grassy leaves which appear only fleetingly in the spring, just long enough to form a flower stalk and seed pod, and then disappear. Flowers, too, last for only a brief period—less than a day. The flowers are a beautiful blue-purple and are very distinct in form with large flat standards and upright style arm crests. It grows in sunny mountain meadows at high altitudes.

It has an uncommon root form among all irises. There is no rhizome to speak of; instead the roots are thick, fleshy, and almost tuberous. It is usually compared to the thick roots of *Hemerocallis,* and this is an apt comparison. The occurrence of thick storage roots suggests that this species must have to withstand severe conditions at some time, conditions that might include drought or cold temperatures. I suspect some of both in its environment. Its occurrence as a high mountain species near the tropics suggests a plant difficult to cultivate, but it apparently is not difficult. Unfortunately it is not widely grown and little information is available about its best care.

It is relatively hardy and seems unspecialized as to soil type.

The specialized rootstock and the absence of a rhizome restrict propagation to seed. *Iris decora* is easy to grow from seed and will bloom quickly from seed. Elaine Hulbert reports that plants have bloomed the year after planting in Virginia.

A third species in this genus, *I. staintonii,* was described in 1974 from central Nepal. Its range may well be found to include adjacent areas of Tibet. Living material has not been introduced into cultivation.

Subgenus *Nepalensis*

Cultivation Basics: Fairly easy with care, but for the specialist.
SOIL Average.
WATER Average.
EXPOSURE Sun.
HARDINESS Not clear, but at least to Zone 6.
SPECIAL NEEDS Needs careful observation and labeling because it is small, comes up late, flowers quickly, and disappears.
AVAILABILITY Uncommon to Available. *I. colletti* is Rare.

SUBGENUS *IRIS:* BEARDED IRISES

There are three true bearded species (section *Iris*) recorded in Zhao's account of Chinese *Iris.* Two of these are cultivated, *Iris* × *germanica* and *I. pallida*. There are many cultivars of German, or tall bearded iris, in gardens in China. Compared to Western interest in these hybrids, the Chinese cultivars are older and of little interest. There does not seem to be any large scale hybridization or selection for tall bearded iris cultivars in China. The only native species in this section is *Iris scariosa*. This is a typical-looking standard dwarf bearded iris that is endemic to Russia and spills over through the Tian Shan Mountains to extreme northwest China in the province of Xinjiang. Zhao describes the Chinese species with violet flowers, but in cultivation there are forms with other colors from blue to reddish purple, yellow, and white-flowered cultivars. The form from the Tian Shan Mountains is said to be slightly larger than the typical Russian form. It should be cultivated like other dwarf bearded iris and should be remarkably hardy. I doubt that any Chinese material is in cultivation.

Iris scariosa

Cultivation Basics: Easy, treated like a typical dwarf bearded iris.

SOIL Average with good drainage.

WATER Average to dry.

EXPOSURE Sun.

HARDINESS Zone 4 easily and perhaps most of Zone 3.

SPECIAL NEEDS None, although it benefits from summer heat and drying.

AVAILABILITY Uncommon to Available.

SECTION *PSEUDOREGELIA:* PSEUDOREGELIA IRISES

This is a fairly large group of primarily Chinese species that is not well known in cultivation anywhere. *Iris kemaonensis* is the most widely grown, but most are unknown. I have seen *Iris mandshurica* and *I. tigridia* growing in Jilin Province and Inner Mongolia respectively and *I. sichuanensis* in Sichuan. I observed that all the pseudoregelia irises seem to have more or less thick fleshy storage roots and lack a rhizome. The presence of these thick roots indicates storage of food and/or water in harsh environments. *Iris mandshurica* in Jilin lives in a cold temperate climate where winters reach −29° C (−20° F), while summer can exceed 37.8° C (100° F). Rainfall is low, 50 cm (20 in) or less per year. I saw *Iris mandshurica* growing on open grassy hillsides and high pastures in full sun. Good drainage seems essential. *Iris tigridia* grows in more extreme climates where rainfall is highly seasonal and restricted to 25 to 50 cm (10 to 20 in) per year. *Iris tigridia* is sometimes found in the light shade of deciduous shrubs. Both of these are quite small plants, reaching about 15 cm (6 in) at flowering with leaves up to twice that length in later growth. *Iris sichuanensis* grows in a much milder climate, but is found in open areas of nearly bare rock on steep hillsides where again drainage is excellent (Figure 31). The roots are less thick and fleshy than those of other species, but they are also longer and may serve to anchor the plant firmly between and in rocks. It is the largest species in this section. Along the rocky slopes of the Min River in Central Sichuan, the iris grows in small pockets of loose soil of less than a teacup in volume. Almost half of the species in this section are very poorly known in the wild or in cultivation. The newly described *Iris dolichosiphon* is cultivated in the rock garden of the Royal Botanical Garden in Edinburgh and is considered hardy there.

The remaining species cover a range of habitats but commonly occur at high elevations, northern latitudes, and in areas with low rainfall. These irises do not produce wide-ranging rhizomes, but they can be propagated by careful divisions of a clump after flowering. Seeds are rarely available, but should be sown in spring.

Section *Pseudoregelia*

Cultivation Basics: Moderate to difficult.
SOIL Average with good drainage.
WATER Average to dry.
EXPOSURE Full sun although light to moderate shade might be best in areas with intense summer sun for some species.
HARDINESS Variable. Most will grow through Zones 5 and 6. *Iris mandshurica* and *I. tigridia* will probably do well through Zone 3. *I. sichuanensis* may not succeed beyond Zones 6 and 7.
SPECIAL NEEDS Specific cultivation requirements have yet to be determined for most species.
AVAILABILITY Most species Uncommon, others Rare.

SECTION *PSAMMIRIS:* SAND IRISES

This small group of only three species has been the source of considerable confusion, as indicated earlier. The species are commonly known as sand irises because of their seeming preference for growing in sandy soils in cold climates. They are stoloniferous iris that die down completely in winter to underground storage stems. *I. flavissima* in Jilin Province and Inner Mongolia grows on nearly pure sand at the edge of cultivated fields at low elevations.

They can be grown like the similar-appearing dwarf bearded iris with emphasis on good drainage, full sun, and summer drying off. Propagation is by division when summer dormant or by seed in spring.

Sand irises

Cultivation Basics: Easy to moderate.
SOIL Average.
WATER Average to dry.
EXPOSURE Sun to light shade.
HARDINESS Zone 4 and most of Zone 3 perhaps further north.
SPECIAL NEEDS Good drainage, especially sandy soils.
AVAILABILITY Uncommon to Rare.

GENUS *PARDANTHOPSIS:* VESPER IRIS

This species was long known as *Iris dichotoma,* the Vesper Iris, and was a more popularly grown iris in Victorian times. Later separated into the genus *Pardanthopsis,* it is obviously closely related to both the genus *Iris* and the vegetatively similar genus *Belamcanda.* The Vesper Iris is so named for its habit of opening its flowers in late afternoon (at vespers) and remaining open for only a few hours. Although the flower is distinctly iris-like in form and color, it blooms in late summer—as early as late July—and the plant form is unlike that of most other irises. The spent flowers twirl as they wither like the related Blackberry Lily (*Belamcanda chinensis*).

Although much has been written about the relationship between the Vesper Iris to the Blackberry Lily, and the hybrid Candy Lilies (× *Pardancanda norrisii*), there seem to be at least two lines of Candy Lilies in cultivation. In the larger and more commercially available line, the flowers have the form of *Belamcanda,* with six nearly equal petals. Flower colors include one-colored forms and those with various patterns of stripes, spots, and mottles. The color range includes red, yellow, orange, purple, and white. The second less common line, also known as × *Pardancanda,* retains the iris-like flower form of *P. dichotoma* and flower colors are restricted to single-tone flowers in the purple, yellow, pink, or white tones.

In China the typical species has flowers of dull off-white with tan and lilac marks. Most cultivated forms have brighter colors of lilac to purple, and all-white forms have been recorded. In Manchuria and Inner Mongolia *Pardanthopsis dichotoma* is common in very open dry grassland in areas of low rainfall. It is obviously able to withstand harsh conditions and climatic extremes of winter cold, summer heat, and near drought.

Because of its delicate-appearing flowers I have always given it some tender treatment, but after observing it growing on the dry, nearly barren hillsides of Inner Mongolia, I realize it can withstand lots of neglect and a wide range of growing conditions. It is very hardy and tolerant. It is not long lived, but readily propagates from seed. Selected forms with good color or large flowers must be propagated by division. One named all-white cultivar, known as 'Summer Snow', must be propagated from division although it produces all-white flowered seedlings.

Pardanthopsis dichotoma

Cultivation Basics: Easy.
SOIL Average.
WATER Average and can withstand dry.
EXPOSURE Sun, but can tolerate light shade.
HARDINESS Zone 3.
SPECIAL NEEDS None.
AVAILABILITY Common to Available.

中國 的 鳶尾

PART II

The Iris of China

by

Zhao Yu-tang

translated by

Youngjune Chang

Foreword to the English Translation

The iris, called "Yuan Wei" in China, meaning "tail of the kite," derives its common name from the shape of the leaves. The typical Chinese species is *Iris tectorum* Thunb. The iris resources of China are very rich; some are famous flowers and plants cultivated around the world, such as *Iris tectorum, I. chrysographes, I. ensata (I. kaempferi)*, and *I. sanguinea*. Their cultivation and hybridization have not been of major interest to Chinese horticulturists.

This English publication of the *Iris* part of the *Flora Reipublicae Popularis Sinicae,* translated by Mr. Youngjune Chang and edited by Dr. James Waddick and Ms. Jean Witt, is very important for Chinese horticulturists. I believe that it will establish a bridge between China and the world of horticulture. This publication will help the world's gardeners to understand Chinese horticulture. I hope that Chinese interest in the cultivation of iris will catch up to that of the rest of the world. Finally, I hope the readers of this book will find enjoyment and encouragement in these pages.

Zhao Yu-tang

FLORA
REIPUBLICAE POPULARIS SINICAE

DELECTIS FLORAE REIPUBLICAE POPULARIS SINICAE

AGENDAE ACADEMIAE SINICAE EDITA

TOMUS 16 (1)

Science Press
1985

Angiospermae

Monocotyledoneae

Iridaceae

Iris

Author: Zhao Yu-tang

N. E. Normal University

IRIS FAMILY—IRIDACEAE

10. Genus Iris—*Iris* L.

Subgenus 1. Beardless Subgenus—Subgen. *Limniris* (Tausch) Spach em. Rodion.

Section 1. Beardless Section—Sect. *Limniris* Tausch
1. Yellow-Flowered Iris   *I. wilsonii* C. H. Wright
2. Yunnan Iris   *I. forrestii* Dykes
3. North Tombs Iris   *I. typhifolia* Kitagawa
4. Jade Cicada Flower   *I. ensata* Thunb.
5. Gold-Veined Iris   *I. chrysographes* Dykes
6. Siberian Iris   *I. sibirica* L.
7. Bloodred Iris·   *I. sanguinea* Donn ex Horn.
8. Southwest Iris   *I. bulleyana* Dykes
9. Long-Scape Iris   *I. delavayi* Mich.
10. Tibet Iris   *I. clarkei* Baker
11. Swallow Flower   *I. laevigata* Fisch.
12. Ussuri Iris   *I. maackii* Maxim.
13. Yellow-Flag Iris   *I. pseudacorus* L.
14. Varied-Color Iris   *I. versicolor* L.
15. Small Yellow-Flowered Iris   *I. minutoaurea* Makino
16. Long-Tail Iris   *I. rossii* Baker
17. Long-Pedicel Iris   *I. henryi* Baker
18. Mountain Iris   *I. setosa* Pall. ex Link
19. White-Flowered Chinese Iris   *I. lactea* Pall.
20. Slender-Leaf Iris   *I. tenuifolia* Pall.
21. Tiny Iris   *I. kobayashi* Kitagawa
22. Qinghai Iris   *I. qinghainica* Y. T. Zhao
23. Cathay Iris   *I. cathayensis* Migo
24. Tian Shan Mountain Iris   *I. loczyi* Kanitz
25. Many-Spotted Iris   *I. polysticta* Diels
26. Songar Iris   *I. songarica* Schrenk
27. Large-Bract Iris   *I. bungei* Maxim.
28. Pouch-Flowered Iris   *I. ventricosa* Pall.

Section 2. Purple-Bract Iris Section—Sect. *Ioniris* Spach em. Rodion.
29. Purple-Bract Iris   *I. ruthenica* Ker-Gawl.
30. Single-Flowered Iris   *I. uniflora* Pall. ex Link

Section 3. Single-Bract Iris Section—Sect. *Ophioiris* Y. T. Zhao
31. Single-Bract Iris   *I. anguifuga* Y. T. Zhao

Subgenus 2. Piano-Valve Iris Subgenus—Subgen. *Xyridion* (Tausch) Spach em. Rodion.
    32. Salt-Loving Iris   *I. halophila* Pall.

Subgenus 3. Nepal Iris Subgenus—Subgen. *Nepalensis* (Dykes) Lawr.
    33. Plateau Iris   *I. collettii* Hook. f.
    34. Nepal Iris   *I. decora* Wall.

Subgenus 4. Field Iris Subgenus—Subgen. *Pardanthopsis* (Hance) Baker
    35. Vesper Iris   *I. dichotoma* Pall.
    36. Zhongdian Iris   *I. subdichotoma* Y. T. Zhao

Subgenus 5. Cockscomb Crested Subgenus—Subgen. *Crossiris* Spach
    Section 1. Cockscomb Crested Section—Sect. *Crossiris* Spach
        37. Small-Flowered Iris   *I. speculatrix* Hance
        38. Taiwan Iris   *I. formosana* Ohwi
        39. Butterfly Flower   *I. japonica* Thunb.
        40. Flat-Bamboo Orchid   *I. confusa* Sealy
        41. Fan-Shaped Iris   *I. wattii* Baker
        42. Wide-Styled Iris   *I. latistyla* Y. T. Zhao
        43. Roof Iris   *I. tectorum* Maxim.
        44. Red-Flowered Iris   *I. milesii* Baker ex M. Foster
    Section 2. Small Iris Section—Sect. *Lophiris* Tausch em. Rodion.
        45. Small Iris   *I. proantha* Diels

Subgenus 6. Bearded Subgenus—Subgen. *Iris*
    Section 1. Fruit Apex-Opening Section—Sect. *Iris*
        46. German Iris   *I. germanica* L.
        47. Fragrant-Root Iris   *I. pallida* Lam.
    Section 2. Fruit Side-Splitting Section—Sect. *Hexapogon* (Bunge) Baker em. Rodion.
        48. Curved-Leaf Iris   *I. curvifolia* Y. T. Zhao
        49. Manchurian Iris   *I. mandshurica* Maxim.
        50. Central Asian Iris   *I. bloudowii* Ledeb.
        51. Gold-Bearded Iris   *I. flavissima* **Pall.**
        52. Membrane-Bract Iris   *I. scariosa* **Willd. ex Link**
        53. Gansu Iris   *I. pandurata* Maxim.
        54. Sichuan Iris   *I. sichuanensis* Y. T. Zhao
        55. Thin-Leaf Iris   *I. leptophylla* Lingelsheim

56. Narcissus Iris   *I. narcissiflora* Diels
57. Curled-Sheath Iris   *I. potaninii* Maxim.
58. Thick-Root Iris   *I. tigridia* Bunge
59. Angular-Fruited Iris   *I. goniocarpa* Baker
60. Kumon Iris   *I. kemaonensis* D. Don ex Royle

10. *Iris* L.

L. Sp. Pl. ed. 1, 38. 1753, et Gen. Pl. ed. 5, 59. 1754; Benth. et Hook. f. Gen. Pl. 3:686–687. 1882; Dykes, Gen. Iris 1913; Lawrence in Gent. Herb. 8(4):346–371. 1953; Rodion. The Genus Iris—*Iris* L. 1961.

Perennial herbs. Stem a rootlike rhizome or bulbous; creeping or ascending, thick or thin. Leaves mostly basal, equitant, two ranked, ensiform, sword shaped or linear, venation parallel, midrib obvious or none, basal portions sheathing, apex acuminate. Generally with obvious flower stalk, but without obvious stem, flower stems emerging from between the leaves, or directly from the ground, rarely short; apex branched or unbranched. Inflorescence racemose or paniculate with solitary flowers; flowers clustered with several membranous or coriaceous bracts, flowers relatively large, blue-purple, purple, reddish purple, yellow or white; perianth tube trumpet shaped, linear, or very short and not obvious, perianth of six petaloid segments in two series, outer petaloid segments (falls) three, with a haft beardless, crested or bearded, inner petaloid segments (standards) three, erect or spreading outward; stamens three emerging from the base of falls, anthers opening outward, filaments distinct from the base of the style; style one, branches three, forked beyond the stigma, ovary inferior, with three cells, placenta axile, ovules several. Capsules elliptical, ovate or orbicular, apex with points or not, splitting open when ripe, seed pear shaped, flattened, orbiculate or irregularly multiangled with or without arils.

Type species of the genus: *Iris germanica* L. (German Iris). Native to Europe, cultivated everywhere in China.

Three hundred species worldwide, distributed in the Northern Temperate zones; in China there are 60 species, 13 varieties, and five forms, with the main distributions in southwest, northwest, and northeast.

CLASSIFYING CHARACTERISTICS

Subgenus 1. Beardless Subgenus   Subgen. *Limniris* (Tausch) Spach em. Rodion. Rhizomes obvious, roots ropelike, not thickened and spindle shaped; perianth tube obvious; falls obovate without a beard or crest on midrib; capsules generally without a beak; seed pear shaped, semiorbicular or orbicular usually without wings.

Section 1. Beardless Section   Sect. *Limniris* Tausch   Style split down to base; after flower drops, perianth tube not persistent on fruit. (Species 1–28)

Section 2. Purple-Bract Iris Section   Sect. *Ioniris* Spach em. Rodion.   Rhizome thin; one flower on each flower stalk, seed glossy. (Species 29–30)

Section 3. Single-Bract Iris Section   Sect. *Ophioiris* Y. T. Zhao Stem evergreen in winter, withered in summer; rhizomes large and coarse, swollen and round at ground level; one bract. (Species 31)

Subgenus 2. Piano-Valve Iris Subgenus   Subgen. *Xyridion* (Tausch) Spach em. Rodion.   Falls pandurate; capsule with distinct points and six angled ridges; seed coat membranous. (Species 32)

Subgenus 3. Nepal Iris Subgenus   Subgen. *Nepalensis* (Dykes) Lawr.   Rhizome very small; roots fleshy, fat, and spindle shaped. (Species 33–34)

Subgenus 4. Vesper Iris Subgenus   Subgen. *Pardanthopsis* (Hance) Baker   Flower stalk branched; with or without perianth tube; falls without beard or crest; seed with small wings. (Species 35–36)

Subgenus 5. Cockscomb Crested Subgenus   Subgen. *Crossiris* Spach   With crest on midrib of falls.

Section 1. Cockscomb Crested Section   Sect. *Crossiris* Spach   Flower stem with two to three (may be five to seven) flowers. Seed with or without an aril. (Species 37–44)

Section 2. Small Iris Section   Sect. *Lophiris* Tausch em. Rodion.   Stem short; flower stem with only one flower. (Species 45)

Subgenus 6. Bearded Subgenus   Subgen. *Iris*   Falls with a beard.

Section 1. Fruit Apex-Opening Section   Sect. *Iris*   Capsules open from the top with three valves. (Species 46–47)

Section 2. Fruit Side-Splitting Section   Sect. *Hexapogon* (Bunge) Baker em. Rodion.   Capsules not open from the top, but on two sides. (Species 48–60)

KEY TO SPECIES

1. Roots fleshy, middle part fat and spindle shaped; rhizome extremely short, but not tuberous, nodes inconspicuous.
  2. Flower stem very short, not emerging from ground; perianth tube 5 to 7 cm long .... 33. *I. collettii* Hook f.
  2. Flower stem relatively long, emerging from ground; perianth tube 2.5 to 3 cm long................. 34. *I. decora* Wall.
1. Roots not fleshy, middle part not fat and spindle shaped; rhizome long and tuberous, nodes conspicuous.
  3. Flower stem dichotomously branched.
    4. Base of stem without brown hairlike old leaf fibers; leaves falcate, apex recurved; perianth tube extremely short ..
    .... 35. *I. dichotoma* Pall.
    4. Base of stem with brown hairlike old leaf fibers; leaves erect or apex slightly incurved; perianth tube about 2 cm long .... 36. *I. subdichotoma* Y. T. Zhao
  3. Flower stem not dichotomously branched or not obvious.
    5. Falls without beard or crest (a few species with single cell cilia).
      6. Falls not pandurate.
        7. Flower stem with several slender branches; leaves over 1.2 cm wide.
          8. Flowers yellow.
            9. Flowers 5 to 5.5 cm diameter; leaf midrib not obvious .... 12. *I. maackii* Maxim.
            9. Flowers 10 to 11 cm diameter; leaf midrib obvious................ 13. *I. pseudacorus* L.
          8. Flowers blue or violet.
            10. Flowers blue, middle of fall with white ringlike marks and speckles..............
            .... 10. *I. clarkei* Baker

10. Flowers violet; middle of fall without white ringlike marks and speckles.
   11. Falls widely obovate. Standards about 2.5 cm long with a sharply acute point . . . .
   . . . . 18. *I. setosa* Pall. ex Link.
   11. Falls oblanceolate. Standards about 3 cm long without a sharply acute point . . . .
   . . . . 14. *I. versicolor* L.
7. Flower stem unbranched or with one or two short branches or without obvious flower stem; leaves less than 1.2 cm wide.
  12. Plants forming clumps; rhizome woody.
    13. Rhizome not tuberous, oblique, encircled by uneven old leaf sheaths and fibers; perianth tube 3 mm long . . . . 19. *I. lactea* Pall.
    13. Rhizome tuberous, encircled by subequal old leaf sheaths; perianth tube 3 to 7 mm long or longer.
      14. Flower stem obvious, emerging 25 cm above the ground; perianth tube 3 to 7 mm long.
        15. Flowers yellow with purplish brown netted pattern. . . . .
        . . . . 25. *I. polysticta* Diels
        15. Flowers violet without purplish brown netted patterns. . . . .
        . . . . 26. *I. songarica* Schrenk
      14. Flower stem not obvious, not emerging or barely emerging from the ground; perianth tube up to 1 cm or longer.
        16. Bracts enlarged, wide-ovate or widely lanceolate.
          17. Transverse veins not forming a net across parallel veins on bracts. . . . . 27. *I. bungei* Maxim.
          17. Transverse veins form net across parallel veins on bracts. . . . . 28. *I. ventricosa* Pall.
        16. Bracts not enlarged, lanceolate or narrowly lanceolate.
          18. Leaves filiform, less than 2 mm wide . . . . . . 20. *I. tenuifolia* Pall.

18. Leaves narrow, linear, more than 2 mm wide.
    19. Leaves less than 20 cm long; flowers less than 5 cm in diameter.
        20. Flowers blue with yellow markings; about 3 cm in diameter; apex of style crest filiform to narrowly deltoid. . . . . .
           21. *I. kobayashii* Kitagawa
        20. Flowers violet or blue without yellow markings; 4.5 to 5 cm in diameter; style crests narrowly lanceolate to deltoid . . . .
           22. *I. qinghainica* Y. T. Zhao
    19. Leaves more than 20 cm long; flowers more than 5 cm in diameter.
        21. Old leaf sheaths brownish red, leaves soft and pendulous; falls narrowly oblanceolate about 5 mm wide. . . . .
           23. *I. cathayensis* Migo
        21. Old leaf sheaths brown; leaves tough and upright; falls oblanceolate or narrowly obovate; 1 to 2 cm wide. . . . .
        . . . . . 24. *I. loczyi* Kanitz
12. Plants not forming clumps; rhizome not woody.
    22. Every flower stem with a solitary flower.
        23. Rhizome thickened, fleshy, close to surface, enlarged globular; one bract . . . .
           31. *I. anguifuga* Y. T. Zhao et X. J. Xue
        23. Rhizome not thickened, fleshy, enlarged, globular; two bracts.

24. Flower yellow; rhizome thin, long, filiform . . . .
. . . . 15. *I. minutoaurea* Makino
24. Flowers violet; rhizome not filiform.
  25. Perianth tube 5 to 7 cm long; bracts narrowly lanceolate, apex long acuminate. . . . .
. . . . 16. *I. rossii* Baker
  25. Perianth tube less than 1.5 cm long; bracts lanceolate or widely lanceolate, apex short acuminate.
    26. Bracts soft, membranous; green with reddish purple edge. . . . .
. . 29. *I. ruthenica* Ker-Gawl.
    26. Bracts hard dry-membranous, yellowish green; with pale red edge . . . .
30. *I. uniflora* Pall. ex Link
22. Every flower stem with two flowers at the apex.
  27. Rhizome thin; flower 2.5 to 3 cm in diameter; bracts narrowly lanceolate . .
. . . . 17. *I. henryi* Baker
  27. Rhizome thicker; flower more than 6 cm in diameter; bracts lanceolate.
    28. Flower yellow to yellowish green.
      29. Standards flaring outward; haft of falls with purple ear-shaped projections . . . .
. . . . . 1. *I. wilsonii* C. H. Wright
      29. Standards erect. Haft of falls without ear-shaped projections. . . . . . . 2. *I. forrestii* Dykes
    28. Flower purple, violet, blue, or white.
      30. Leaves with midrib obvious.
        31. Leaves narrowly linear, about 2 mm wide; bracts membranous, apex acuminate, parallel veins not obvious. . . . .
. . . . 3. *I. typhifolia* Kitagawa

31. Leaves linear; 0.5 to 1.2 cm
wide; bracts almost coriaceous, apex acute or obtuse,
parallel veins obvious . . . .
. . . . 4. *I. ensata* Thunb.
30. Leaves without obvious midrib.
32. Standards flared outward to
pendulous.
33. Flower stem 25 to 50 cm
high, about 5 mm in
diameter; falls with
gold-yellow markings
. . . . . 5. *I. chrysographes*
Dykes
33. Flower stem 60 to 120
cm high, 5 to 7 mm in
diameter; falls with
white to deep purple
mottling . . . .
. . . . 9. *I. delavayi* Mich.
32. Standards erect.
34. Flower 9 to 10 cm in
diameter; style crests
1.5 to 2 cm long . . . . . .
. . . 11. *I. laevigata* Fisch.
34. Flower less than 9 cm in
diameter; style crests
less than 1.5 cm long.
35. Falls with brown
netted pattern on
hafts.
36. Flower violet or
deep bluish
purple; fruit
ovate cylindri-
cal shaped, two
to three times
longer than
wide . . . .
. . 6. *I. sibirica* L.
36. Flower sky
blue, violet;
fruit long ovate

cylindrical, three to four times longer than wide.....
.. 7. *I. sanguinea* Donn ex Horn.

35. Falls with blue-purple mottled spots and stripes..
..... 8. *I. bulleyana* Dykes

6. Falls pandurate .... 32. *I. halophila* Pall.
5. Falls with beard or crest.
   37. Falls with crest.
     38. Stem not obvious; leaves all basal.
       39. Flower stem not branched or with one or two side branches.
         40. Rhizome not obvious; roots long and thick; style arm about 1.5 cm wide, terminal lobes clustered near center of flower .... 42. *I. latistyla* Y. T. Zhao
         40. Rhizome obvious; roots short and thin; style arm narrow, terminal lobes clustered in center of flower.
           41. Rhizome 1 cm in diameter; leaves 1.5 to 3.5 cm wide; flower 10 cm in diameter; crest irregular ....
.... 43. *I. tectorum* Maxim.
           41. Rhizome less than 1 cm in diameter; leaves less than 1.5 cm wide; flower less than 6 cm in diameter; crest even.
              42. Leaves 6 to 12 mm wide; rhizome not filiform; nodes not inflated; fruiting stalk bent at a 90° angle .... 37. *I. speculatrix* Hance
              42. Leaves 1 to 7 mm wide; rhizome slender, filiform; nodes inflated; fruiting stalk not bent ....
.... 45. *I. proantha* Diels
       39. Flower stem branched.
         43. Flower stem with four to five branches; flowers white, 7 to 8 cm in diameter ...
.... 38. *I. formosana* Ohwi

43. Flower stem with 5 to 12 branches; flowers violet or pale blue, 4.5 to 5.5 cm in diameter .... 39. *I. japonica* Thunb.
38. Stem obvious; leaves alternate on stem or grouped at stem apex.
    44. Leaves grouped at stem apex, arranged in a fan; flowers violet, pale blue or white.
        45. Flower pale blue or white, 5 to 5.5 cm in diameter .... 40. *I. confusa* Sealy
        45. Flower violet, 7.5 to 8 cm in diameter .... 41. *I. wattii* Baker
    44. Leaves alternate on stem, not arranged in a terminal fan; flowers pale reddish purple .... 44. *I. milesii* Baker ex M. Foster
37. Falls with beard.
    46. Plant up to 1 meter high; standards obovate or round, about 5 cm wide.
        47. Bracts green, herbaceous with membranous margin................. 46. *I. germanica* L.
        47. Bracts silver-white, completely membranous .... 47. *I. pallida* Lamarck
    46. Plant less than 60 cm high; standards narrowly ovate or oblanceolate.
        48. Flower stem with a single flower.
            49. Standards flaring outward; falls with sparse beard..... 56. *I. narcissiflora* Diels
            49. Standards erect; falls with compact beard.
                50. Old leaves at stem base hairlike coiled outward...... 57. *I. potaninii* Maxim.
                50. Old leaves at stem base not as above.
                    51. Roots not branched and showing transverse marks............. .... 58. *I. tigridia* Bunge
                    51. Roots branched and without transverse marks.
                        52. Flower stem obvious and emerging from the ground; perianth tube 1.5 to 2 cm long .... 59. *I. goniocarpa* Baker
                        52. Flower stem not emerging from ground; perianth tube 5.5 to 6 cm long..........

.... 60. *I. kemaonensis*
D. Don ex Royle
48. Flower stem with two flowers, rarely one.
53. Flowers yellow.
54. Leaves sickle shaped or curved above the middle part.
55. Leaves with a swollen sheath; bracts lanceolate; fruit apex rounded, beak very short ......
.... 48. *I. curvifolia* Y. T. Zhao
55. Leaves without a swollen sheath; bracts obovate or oblanceolate; fruit apex acuminate to form a long beak ....
...... 49. *I. mandshurica* Maxim.
54. Leaves not curved or slightly curved.
56. Flower stem emerging from the ground, 8 to 10 cm high ....
.... 50. *I. bloudowii* Ledeb.
56. Flower stem not or barely emerging from the ground .....
.... 51. *I. flavissima* Pall.
53. Flowers blue or violet.
57. Leaves curved, sickle shaped ......
.... 52. *I. scariosa.* Willd. ex Link
57. Leaves not curved.
58. Roots long and thick; plant base with many yellowish brown hairlike old leaf fibers ....
.... 53. *I. pandurata* Maxim.
58. Roots thin and short; plant base with few yellowish brown hairlike old leaf fibers and membranous sheathlike leaves.
59. Flower about 6 cm in diameter; leaves 0.5 to 1 cm wide
54. *I. sichuanensis* Y. T. Zhao
59. Flower 3.5 to 4 cm in diameter. Leaves 2 to 3 mm wide
55. *I. leptophylla* Lingelsheim

Subgenus 1. Beardless Subgenus—Subgen. *Limniris* (Tausch) Spach in Ann. Sci. Nat. ser. 3, 5. 99. 1846; em Rodion. The Genus Iris—*Iris* L. 185. 1961—*Iris* Sect. *Limniris* Tausch in Hort. Canalius, 1. 1823.

Section 1. Beardless Section—Sect. *Limniris* Tausch in Hort. Canalius 1. 1823.

1. **Yellow-Flowered Iris** (Flora of Qin Ling) Plate A:1–3

Iris wilsonii C. H. Wright in Kew Bull. 321. 1907; Stapf in Curtis's Bot. Mag. t. 8340. 1910; Dykes, Gen. Iris 26, pl. 12. 1913; Liu Yin, Chinese Magazine of Botany 3(2):941. 1936; Flora of Qin Ling 1(1): 389, Fig. 379. 1976.

Perennial herb, stem base with persistent old leaf fibers. Rhizome thick and creeping. Roots yellowish white with few branches. Leaves basal, gray-green, linear 25 to 55 cm long, 5 to 8 mm wide, apex acuminate with three to five nonprojecting veins. Flower stem hollow, 50 to 60 cm with one or two leaflets; bracts three, herbaceous, green, lanceolate 6 to 9 (16) cm long, 0.8 to 1 cm wide, apex long-acuminate with an obvious midrib, containing two flowers. Flower yellow, 6 to 7 cm in diameter, pedicel thin 3 to 11 cm long; perianth tube 0.5 to 1.2 cm long. Falls obovate, 6 to 6.5 cm long about 1.5 cm wide with purple-brown stripes and mottled spots. Hafts of falls narrowly cuneiform with purple-brown auricles on both sides. Standards oblanceolate, 4.5 to 5 cm long, 7 mm wide, slanting outward when in full bloom. Stamen about 3.5 cm long, anther and filament almost the same length. Style arm deep yellow, 4.5 to 6 cm long, crests obtuse-deltoid or semirounded. Ovary green 1.2 to 1.8 cm long. Capsule elliptical-cylindrical, 3 to 4 cm long, 1.5 to 2 cm in diameter with six obvious ribs, apex without points. Opening when ripe from the apex down to the middle. Seed brown flattened, semirounded. Flowering May to June, fruiting July to August.

Native to Hubei, Shaanxi, Gansu, Sichuan, and Yunnan. Grows among grasses on hillsides from the forest edge to damp riversides. Type specimen from Fang County in Western Hubei.

2. **Yunnan Iris** (English Latin Chinese Plant Names) Big Purple Gladiolus (Yunnan Plant List) Plate A:4–5

Iris forrestii Dykes in Gard. Chron. ser. 3, 47:418. 1910, et Gen. Iris 27, pl. 3. 1913; Liu Yin, Chinese Magazine of Botany 3(2):941. 1936; Bailey, Man. Cult. Pl. 175. 1949.

Perennial herb, stem base with persistent sheathlike leaves or old leaves which persist as fibers. Rhizome creeping, about 5 mm in

diameter, brown; roots yellowish white. Leaves linear, yellowish green, 20 to 50 cm long, 4 to 7 mm wide, apex acuminate, base sheathlike without obvious midrib. Flower stem glabrous, yellowish green 15 to 45 cm high, 2 to 3 mm in diameter with one to three leaflets; bracts three, membranous, green, upper part slightly reddish purple, lanceolate, 5.5 to 7 cm long, 1 to 1.2 cm wide, apex long acuminate, or spreading and leaflike; containing one or two flowers. Flowers yellow, 6.5 to 7 cm in diameter; pedicel 3.5 to 5 cm long; perianth tube funnel-form about 1.3 cm long. Falls obovate about 6.5 cm long, about 2.5 cm wide with purple-brown stripes and mottled spots, haft of fall narrowly cuneiform, beardless. Standards erect. Stamen about 3 cm long, anthers brownish yellow, filaments and anthers almost the same size. Style arms pale yellow, 4 to 4.5 cm long, 1.4 to 1.6 cm wide, crests obtuse-deltoid, ovary green triangular-cylindrical about 2 cm long. Capsule obtuse-elliptical, 4 to 4.5 cm long, 1.5 to 1.8 cm in diameter with a short point and six obvious ribs, splitting when ripe. Seed flattened, semirounded. Flowering May to June, fruiting July to August.

Native to Sichuan, Yunnan, and Tibet. Grows at an altitude of 2750 to 3600 m in ditches, damp areas of stream sides or among grass on hillsides. Also native to Burma. Type specimen from Yunnan.

3. **North Tombs Iris** (Key to Northeast Plants) Cattail-Leaved Iris (Key to the Flora of Northeastern China) Plate B:1–3
Iris typhifolia Kitagawa in Bot. Mag. Tokyo 48:94, f. 10. 1934, et Lineam. Fl. Mansh. 149. 1939; Key to Northeast Plants 586. 1959.
Perennial herb, stem base reddish with persistent lanceolate and sheath-shaped leaves and old fibrous leaves. Rhizome relatively thick and creeping, roots grayish white to grayish brown, both upper and lower parts equally thick. Leaves linear, twisted, at flowering 30 to 40 cm long, 2 mm wide; at fruiting 90 cm long; 2 to 3 mm wide, apex long acuminate, base sheath shaped, midrib obvious. Flower stem smooth, hollow 50 to 60 cm high with two or three lanceolate leaves. Bracts three or four, membranous, mottled with small brown or reddish brown spots, lanceolate 5.5 to 6 cm long, 1 to 1.2 cm wide, apex acuminate, midrib obvious. Flower

PLATE A   1–3. **Yellow-Flowered Iris** *Iris wilsonii* C. H. Wright: 1. Rhizome. 2. Upper part of stem with flower. 3. Fruiting branch.
4–5. **Yunnan Iris** *Iris forrestii* Dykes: 4. Rhizome. 5. Upper part of stem with flower.
DRAWN BY YU ZHEN-ZHOU AND ZHAO YU-TANG

deep violet, 6 to 7 cm in diameter; pedicel 1 to 5 cm long; perianth tube about 5 mm long. Falls obovate 5 to 5.5 cm long, 2 cm wide, beardless. Standards erect oblanceolate, apex retuse 4.5 to 5 cm long, 1 to 1.2 cm wide, stamens about 3 cm long, anthers yellowish brown, filaments white; style arms about 3.5 cm long, 1 to 1.2 cm wide, crests deltoid. Ovary three ridged, cylindrical 1.5 to 2 cm long, 2 to 3 mm wide. Capsule three ridged elliptical 4.5 to 5 cm long, 1.2 to 1.5 cm in diameter with six veins and three obvious ribs, splitting when ripe. Flowering time May to June, fruiting time July to September.

Native to Jilin, Liaoning, and Inner Mongolia. Grows in damp areas near lakes or other water. Type specimen from Beiling (North Tombs of Qing Dynasty), Shenyang City.

This species differs from *Iris sanguinea* in the following: *Iris typhifolia* leaves narrow, generally about 2 mm wide; flower deep blue purple mottled with small brownish spots; distributed in west of northeast China and in eastern Inner Mongolia.

4. **Jade Cicada Flower** (Dictionary of Botany) Blue Flag (Iconographia Cormophytorum Sinicorum) Purple-Flowered Iris (Key to Northeast Plants) Northeast Iris (Handbook of Cultivated Plants of the Lushan Botanical Garden) Plate B:4–5
Iris ensata Thunb. in Trans. Linn. Soc. 2:328. 1794; Kitagawa, Lineam. Fl. Mansh. 147. 1939;—*I. ensata* Thunb. var *spontanea* (Makino) Nakai, Veg. Mt. Apoi. 78.1930; Makino et Nemoto, Fl. Jap. ed. 2, 1590. 1931; Ohwi, Fl. Jap. 333. 1956;—*I. kaempferi* Sieb. ex Lem. Ill. Hort. 5: t. 157. 1858. p. p.; Dykes, Gen. Iris 74. 1913; Kom. Fl. Mansh. 413. 1927; Liu Yin, Chinese Magazine of Botany 3(2):944. 1936; Key to Northeast Plants 587. 1959; Iconographia Cormophytorum Sinicorum 5:577, Fig. 7984. 1976;—*I. kaempferi* Sieb. ex Lem. α *spontanea* Makino in Bot. Mag. Tokyo 23:94. 1909;—*I. laevigata* Fisch. var. *kaempferi* Maxim. in Bull. Acad. Sci. St. Petersb. 26:521. 1880; B. Fedtsch. in Kom. Fl. URSS 4:525. 1935.
Perennial herb, stem base with persistent leaf sheaths. Rhizome thick and creeping, covered with brownish sheaths and persistent

---

PLATE B   1–3. **North Tombs Iris** *Iris typhifolia* Kitagawa: 1. Lower part of stem with leaves. 2. Upper part of stem with flower. 3. Split capsule.
4–5. **Jade Cicada Flower** *Iris ensata* Thunb.: 4. Lower part of stem. 5. Flowering stem.
6. **Flowering Sweet-Flag** *Iris ensata* Thunb. var. **hortensis** Makino et Nemoto: Part of flower stem and leaf.
DRAWN BY YU ZHEN-ZHOU

fibers; roots cordlike, grayish white with wrinkled transverse pattern. Leaves linear 30 to 80 cm long, 0.5 to 1.2 cm wide, apex acuminate or long-acuminate, bases sheathlike, both sides with obvious midribs. Flower stem cylindrical, 40 to 100 cm high, solid, with one to three leaflets; bracts three almost coriaceous, lanceolate 4.5 to 7.5 cm long, 0.8 to 1.2 cm wide, apex mucronate, acuminate, or obtuse, parallel ribs obvious and raised, containing two flowers; flowers deep purple, 9 to 10 cm in diameter; pedicel 1.5 to 3.5 cm long; perianth tube funnel-form 1.5 to 2 cm long, falls obovate 7 to 8.5 cm long, 3 to 3.5 cm wide, claw slender, midrib mottled with yellow, standards small, erect, narrowly lanceolate or widely strap shaped about 5 cm long, about 5 to 6 mm wide; stamens about 3.5 cm long, anthers purple, filaments longer than anthers; style arms flat about 5 cm long, 0.7 to 1 cm wide, purple, apex deltoid, ovary cylindrical 1.5 to 2 cm long, about 3 mm in diameter. Capsule long-elliptical 4.5 to 5.5 cm long, 1.5 to 1.8 cm wide, apex with short point, six ribs obvious, at ripening capsule splits down one-third from top; seed maroon-brown, flat, semirounded. Flowering time June to July, fruiting in August to September.

Native to Heilongjiang, Jilin, Liaoning, Shandong, and Zhejiang. Grows in damp areas beside lakes or rivers. Also native to Korea, Japan, and Russia. Type specimen from Japan.

Many people use the name *Iris ensata* for *Iris lactea* var. *chinensis*, which is widely distributed in northern China, Korea, and Russia, but use the name *Iris kaempferi* Sieb. ex Lem. (1858) for *Iris ensata*, possibly because Thunberg's original description was too short. After verification, the scientific name for Jade Cicada Flower should be *Iris ensata* Thunb. Since *Iris kaempferi* Sieb. ex Lem. was published in 1858, later than *Iris ensata*, *Iris kaempferi* should be regarded as a junior synonym.

4a. **Flowering Sweet Flag** Plate B:6
var. *hortensis* Makino et Nemoto, Fl. Jap. ed. 2, 1590. 1931;—*I. kaempferi* Sieb. ex Lem. β *hortensis* (Maxim.) Makino, in Bot. Mag. Tokyo 23:95. 1909;—*I. kaempferi* Sieb. ex Lem. Ill. Hort. 5. t. 157. 1858. p.p.
This is a horticultural variety with a great many forms; vegetative parts, flower patterns and colors are variable for each form. Leaves wide strap shaped 50 to 80 cm long, 1 to 1.8 cm wide, midrib obvious and thickened. Flower stem about 1 m high, 5 to 8 mm in diameter; bracts almost coriaceous, veins parallel, obvious and thick, apex obtuse or short acuminate; flowers from white to dark

purple, with various marks and floral patterns, flowers are single to double. Prefers to grow in damp areas, may be cultivated at the edges of creeks, lakes, or ponds, or as a potted plant. Flowering in June to July, fruiting in August to September.

5. **Gold-Veined Iris** (English-Latin Chinese Plant Names) Gold-Pattern Iris (Iconographia Cormophytorum Sinicorum) Gold-Net Iris (Chinese Magazine of Botany) Plate C:1–3

Iris chrysographes Dykes in Gard. Chron. ser. 3, 49:362. 1911; Stapf in Curtis's Bot. Mag. t. 8433. 1912; Dykes, Gen. Iris 28, pl. 4. 1913; Iconographia Cormophytorum Sinicorum 5:577, Fig. 7983. 1976.

Perennial herb, stem base with many maroon lanceolate sheath-shaped leaves. Rhizome cylindrical, maroon brown, creeping, covered with persistent leaf sheaths and maroon membranous sheathlike leaves; roots yellowish white, with wrinkled transverse markings, emerging from the side of rhizome. Leaves basal, gray-green, strap shaped 25 to 70 cm long, 0.5 to 1.2 cm wide, apex acuminate, base sheath shaped, without obvious midrib. Flower stem glabrous and hollow, 25 to 50 cm high, about 0.5 cm in diameter with one or two leaflets on middle or lower part, leaf sheaths wide and surrounding the flower stem; bracts three, green, tinted lightly reddish purple, lanceolate 6.5 to 9 cm long by 0.8 to 1.5 cm wide, apex long-acuminate, containing two flowers; flowers dark violet 8 to 12 cm in diameter; falls narrowly obovate or long-orbicular 5.5 to 7 cm long by 2.5 to 3.5 cm wide with golden yellow striped markings, standards narrowly lanceolate about 6 cm long by about 1 cm wide, inclined outward at flowering; stamens 4 to 4.5 cm long, anthers violet, filaments purple, longer than anthers; style arms dark purple, 4.5 to 5 cm long, 6 to 8 mm wide, crests obtuse, semirounded; ovary three ridged, spindle shaped, green 3 to 3.5 cm long by 5 to 7 mm in diameter. Capsule three ridged, cylindrical, 4 to 6 cm long by 1.7 to 2 cm in diameter, base rounded, apex acuminate, without points; seed almost pomoid, maroon-brown. Flowering in June to July, fruiting in August to October.

Native to Sichuan, Guizhou, Yunnan, and Tibet. Grows at an altitude of 1200 to 4400 m on hillsides or forest edges. Type specimen from Guan county, Sichuan.

6. **Siberian Iris** (Handbook of Cultivated Plants of the Lushan Botanical Garden)

Iris sibirica L. Sp. Pl. 39. 1753; Dykes, Gen. Iris 20, pl. 1 (a). 1913; B. Fedtsch. in Kom. Fl. URSS 4:519. 1935; Bailey, Man. Cult. pl. 275. 1949.

Perennial herb, stem base with sheathlike leaves and persistent fibers. Rhizome thick and creeping; roots yellowish white, cordlike with wrinkled transverse marks. Leaves gray green strap shaped, 20 to 40 cm long by 0.5 to 1 cm wide, apex acuminate, without obvious midrib. Flower stem taller than leaves, smooth 40 to 60 cm high with one or two leaves; bracts three, membranous, green with slightly reddish purple margin, narrowly ovate or lanceolate 4 to 5.5 cm long by 0.8 to 2 cm wide, apex short acuminate, containing two flowers; flowers violet 7.5 to 9 cm in diameter; pedicel extremely short; perianth tube about 1 cm long, falls obovate, 5.5 to 7 cm long by 3.3 to 5 cm wide, outer part pendulous, hafts with brown netted patterns and mottled yellow, without beard or crest, standards narrowly elliptical or oblanceolate 4.5 to 5.5 cm long by 1.5 to 1.8 cm wide, erect; stamens 3 to 3.5 cm long, anthers purple, filaments pale purple; style arms pale blue, 4 to 4.5 cm long, apex semirounded, margin with few irregular teeth; ovary green spindle shaped 1.5 to 2 cm long. Capsule ovate-cylindrical, long-cylindrical, or elliptical-cylindrical, 3.5 to 5.5 cm long by 1.3 to 1.5 cm in diameter without points. Flowering in April to May, fruiting in June to July.

Native to Europe. Cultivated in gardens. Type specimen from Europe.

7. **Bloodred Iris** (Compendium of Materia Medica) Oriental Iris (Chinese Magazine of Botany) Oriental Variety of Siberian Iris (Key to the Flora of Northeast China) Plate C:4–6

Iris sanguinea Donn ex Horn. Hort. Bot. Hafn.1:58. 1813; Bailey, Man. Cult. Pl. 275. 1949; Ohwi, Fl. Jap. 333. 1956;—*I. sanguinea* Donn ex Horn. var. *typica* Makino in Journ. Jap. Bot. 6 (11):32. 1930;—*I. nertschinskia* Lodd. in Bot. Catin 19, t. 1843. 1832–1833; Kitagawa, Lineam. Fl. Mansh. 148. 1939; Makino, New Ill.

PLATE C 1–3. **Gold-Veined Iris** *Iris chrysographes* Dykes: 1. Lower part of stem with rhizome. 2. Upper part of flower stem. 3. Fruiting branch.
4–6. **Bloodred Iris** *Iris sanguinea* Donn ex Horn.: 4. Lower part of stem with rhizome. 5. Flowering branch. 6. Fruiting branch.
7. **Yixing Bloodred Iris** *Iris sanguinea* Donn ex Horn. var. *yixingensis* Y. T. Zhao: Capsule.
DRAWN BY YU ZHEN-ZHOU

Fl. Jap. 867, t. 3467. 1963;—*I. orientalis* auct. non Mill.: Thunb. in Trans. Linn. Soc. 2:328. 1794; Maxim. in Bull. Acad. Sci. St. Petersb. 26:519. 1880; Dykes, Gen. Iris 23. 1913; B. Fedtsch. in Kom. Fl. URSS 4:520. 1935; Liu Yin, Chinese Magazine of Botany 3(2):939. 1936;—*I. sibirica* L. var. *sanguinea* Ker-Gawl. in Curtis's Bot. Mag. t. 1604. 1814;—*I. sibirica* L. var. *orientalis* Baker in Journ. Linn. Soc. Bot. 16:139. 1877; Maxim. in Bull. Acad. Sci. St. Petersb. 26:519. 1880; Kom. Fl. Mansh. 414. 1927;—*I. extremorientalis* Koidz. in Bot. Mag. Tokyo 40:330. 1926; Makino et Nemoto, Fl. Jap. ed. 2, 1591. 1931.

Perennial herb. Rhizome thick and creeping, covered with maroon-brown old leaves which persist as fibers; roots cordlike, grayish white with wrinkled transverse patterns. Leaves strap shaped 20 to 60 cm long by 0.5 to 1.3 cm wide, apex acuminate, base sheathlike, midribs not obvious. Flower stem glabrous and solid 40 to 60 cm high with one or two leaflets; bracts three, membranous, green, lanceolate, 5 to 7 cm long about 1 cm wide, apex acuminate; containing two flowers; flower azure blue, 6 to 7 cm in diameter; perianth tube short and stout 0.8 to 1 cm long by 4 mm in diameter, falls obovate 4.5 to 5 cm long by 1.8 cm wide, base with black-brown netted patterns and yellow mottling, without beard or crest, standards erect, narrowly obovate, about 4.5 cm long by about 1.5 cm wide; stamens about 3 cm long, anthers yellow, filaments white, filiform; style arms flat, about 3.5 cm long by 5 mm wide, crests obtuse-deltoid with fine teeth, ovary three ridged cylindrical 1.5 to 2 cm long by 3 to 4 mm in diameter. Fruit long-ovate cylindrical 3.5 to 5 cm long by 1.2 to 1.5 cm in diameter, three to four times longer than wide, veined with six obvious ridges; at ripening it splits down one-third from the top. Flowering in May to June, fruiting in July to September.

Native to Heilongjiang, Jilin, Liaoning, and Inner Mongolia. Grows near ponds, damp meadows, or sunny banks. Also native to Japan, Korea, and Russia. Type specimen from Japan.

7a. **Yixing Bloodred Iris** Plate C:7

var. *yixingensis* Y. T. Zhao, Acta Phytotaxonomica Sinica 20(1): 99. 1982.

Perennial herb, stem with many membranous sheathlike leaves. Rhizome creeping, upper part with maroon-brown old leaves which persist as fibers; roots, yellow with transverse patterns. Leaves basal, strap shaped, 30 to 50 cm long by 2 to 4 mm wide, apex long-acuminate, base sheathlike, inner surface with silvery white metallic gloss. Flower stem hollow 40 to 60 cm high, one or two leaves on middle or upper-middle part; bracts two or three, outer surface reddish brown, inner surface pale, lanceolate 6 to 7 cm long, by 7 to 9 mm wide, apex acuminate, containing one or two flowers; flowers dark violet 5.5 to 6 cm in diameter; perianth tube extremely short. Fruit three ridged, cylindrical, about 4.5 cm long by 0.8 to 1 cm in diameter, gray-green, surface white-pubescent, apex without obvious point; seed black-brown, flat, semirounded. Flowering in April to May, fruiting in June to August.

Native to Yixing, Jiangsu Province. Grows in damp meadows or mountain stream banks. Type specimen from Yixing, Jiangsu.

7b. **White-Flower Bloodred Iris**
f. *albiflora* Makino in Journal Jap. Bot. 6(11):32. 1930; Makino et Nemoto, Fl. Jap. ed. 2, 1593. 1931.
Flower white.

Native to northeast of Heilongjiang. Grows near ponds or damp meadows or along sides of streams or lakes. Also native to Japan.

8. **Southwest Iris** (Handbook of Cultivated Plants of the Lushan Botanical Garden) Hollow-Stem Iris (English-Latin Chinese Seed Plant Names) Plate D:1–2
Iris bulleyana Dykes in Gard, Chron. ser. 3, 47:418. 1910, et Gen. Iris 30, Pl. 6. 1913; Bailey, Man. Cult. Pl. 275. 1949.
Perennial herb. Rhizome thick and creeping, with persistent reddish brown old leaves and sheathlike leaf bases; roots cordlike, grayish white to maroon-brown, with wrinkled transverse patterns, emerging from the side of rhizome. Leaves basal, strap shaped, 15 to 45 cm long, 0.5 to 1 cm wide, apex acuminate, base sheathlike and slightly red, without obvious midribs. Flower stem hollow, glossy, 20 to 35 cm high, 4 to 6 mm in diameter, with two or three leaves, base with slightly reddish purple sheathlike leaves; bracts two or three, membranous, green, margin slightly reddish brown, 5.5 to 12 cm long, 0.8 to 1.2 cm wide, containing one or two flowers; flowers blue, 6.5 to 7.5 cm in diameter; pedicel 2 to 6 cm long; perianth tube three ridged cylindrical, short and thick, 1 to 1.2 cm long, falls obovate, 4.5 to 5 cm long, about 2.5 cm wide, without crest or beard, with blue-purple mottled and striped pattern, standards erect, lanceolate or widely lanceolate, about 4 cm long by about 1.5 cm wide, light violet, angled slightly outward at flowering; stamens about 2.5 cm long, anthers milky white, filaments longer than anthers; style arms flat, midrib projecting, dark violet, about 3.5 cm long, crests square, margin entire, ovary green, obtuse triangular to cylindrical, about 2 cm long. Capsule three

sided cylindrical, 4 to 5.5 cm long, 1.5 to 1.8 cm in diameter, with six obvious ridges, apex obtuse, without points, always with persistent perianth, outer surface with obvious netted pattern; seeds maroon-brown, flat, semirounded. Flowering in June to July, fruiting in August to October.

Native to Sichuan, Yunnan, and Tibet. Grows at an altitude of 2300 to 3500 m on damp hillside meadows or at creekside. Type specimen from Yunnan.

8a. **White-Flowered Southwest Iris**

f. *alba* Y. T. Zhao, Acta Phytotaxonomica Sinica 18 (1):54. 1980. Flower milky white, other characters the same as those of *Iris bulleyana.*

Native to Yunnan. Grows in meadows on hillsides or damp sites near stream. Type specimen from Yunnan.

9. **Long-Scape** Iris (Yunnan Plant Name List) Plate D:3–5

Iris delavayi Mich. in Rev. Hort. Paris 399, f.128–129. 1895; Hook. f. in Curtis's Bot. Mag. t. 7661. 1899; C. H. Wright in Journ. Linn. Soc. Bot. 36:80. 1903; Dykes, Gen. Iris 25. 1913; Liu Yin, Chinese Magazine of Botany 3(2):939. 1936; Bailey, Man. Cult. Pl. 276. 1949.

Perennial herb, stem base reddish purple with membranous sheathlike leaves and fibrous old leaf sheaths. Rhizome thick and strong, 1 cm in diameter, creeping, covered with maroon-brown old leaves which persist as fibers; roots yellowish white, with wrinkled transverse patterns. Leaves grayish green, sword or strap shaped 50 to 80 cm long by 0.8 to 1.5 cm wide, apex long-acuminate, base sheathlike, without obvious midribs. Flower stem hollow, glabrous, 60 to 120 cm high, 5 to 7 mm in diameter, apex with one or two short branches below the middle with three or four lanceolate leaves; bracts two or three, membranous, green, tinted light reddish purple, broadly lanceolate, 7 to 11 cm long by 1.8 to 2 cm wide, apex long acuminate, containing two flowers. Flowers deep purple or violet with dark purple and white mottled pattern about 9 cm in diameter; pedicel 3 to 6 cm long; perianth tube 1.5 to 1.8 cm long; falls obovate about 7 cm long by about 3 cm wide, apex retuse, blade of falls pendulous at flowering, with dark purple and

---

PLATE D   1–2. **Southwest Iris** *Iris bulleyana* Dykes: 1. Flowering branch. 2. Fruiting branch.
3–5. **Long-Scape Iris** *Iris delavayi* Mich.: 3. Lower part of stem with rhizome. 4. Flowering branch. 5. Fruiting branch.
DRAWN BY YU ZHEN-ZHOU AND ZHAO YU-TANG

white mottling and without beard; standards oblanceolate, 5.5 cm long, inclined outward at flowering; anthers milky yellow, filaments pale purple; style arms pale purple, about 5 cm long by about 1.6 cm wide, crests long-orbicular, ovary cylindrical three ridged, 1.8 to 2 cm long by about 7 mm in diameter. Capsule cylindrical to long-elliptical, 5 to 6.5 cm long by 1.5 to 2.5 cm in diameter, without points; seed reddish brown, flat, disklike about 6 mm in diameter. Flowering in May to July, fruiting in August to October.

Native to Sichuan, Yunnan, and Tibet. Grows at an altitude of 2700 to 3100 m in damp sites along ditches, in meadows, or at the edge of forests. Type specimen from cultivated plant from seeds from Yunnan.

10. **Tibet Iris** Plate E:1–2

Iris clarkei Baker, Handb. Irid. 25. 1892; Hook. f. Fl. Brit. Ind. 6:275. 1892; Dykes in Gard. Chron. ser. 3, 46:15. 1909; Stapf, in Curtis's Bot. Mag. t. 8323. 1910; Dykes Gen. Iris 29. 1913;—*I. himalaica* Dykes in Gard. Chron. ser. 3, 45:3.36. 1910.

Perennial herb. Rhizome cylindrical, creeping, covered with old leaves which persist as fibers. Leaves grayish green, strap or sword shaped, 30 to 60 cm long, 1 to 1.8 cm wide, apex acuminate, base sheath shaped. Flower stem about 60 cm high, about 5 mm in diameter, upper part with two or three branches, lower part with two or three leaflets sheathing the flower stem, leaflets 15 to 25 cm long; bracts three, green, margin membranous, broadly lanceolate, 7.5 to 9 cm long, with obvious midribs, containing one or two flowers; flowers blue, 7.5 to 8.5 cm in diameter; pedicel slender, 2.5 to 3.5 cm long; perianth tube green, short and thick, about 1 cm long, about 5 mm in diameter, falls obovate, about 7 cm long, 2.4 to 2.8 cm wide, center with white ringlike mottled pattern, standards pale violet, oblanceolate, 4 to 4.5 cm long, 1 cm wide, inclined outward at bloom; anthers milky white, shorter than filaments; style arms flat, 4 to 4.5 cm long, about 1 cm wide, crests obtuse, semirounded; ovary green, triangular and spindle shaped, about 2.5 cm long, about 5 mm in diameter. Capsule ovate-cylindrical, 3.5 to 5 cm long, 1.2 to 2.5 cm in diameter, with six obvious veins; seed flat and

PLATE E   1–2. **Tibet Iris** *Iris clarkei* Baker: 1. Upper part of stem with flower stalk. 2. Fruiting branch.
3–6. **Swallow Flower** *Iris laevigata* Fisch.: 3. Lower part of stem with rhizome. 4. Flower. 5. Fruiting branch. 6. Seed.
DRAWN BY YU ZHEN-ZHOU AND ZHAO YU-TANG

disk shaped. Flowering in June to July, fruiting in August to September.

Native to Yunnan and Tibet. Grows along steams or damp sites near lakes. Also distributed in India. Type specimen from Darjeeling, India.

11. **Swallow Flower** (Annals of Zhangzhou Prefecture) Flat-Leaved Iris (Cultivated Plant List of the Beijing Botanical Garden) Glossy-Leaved Iris (Chinese Magazine of Botany) Plate E:3–6

Iris laevigata Fisch. in Turcz. Cat. Baik. 1119. 1837; Fisch. et Mey. Ind. Sem. Hort. Bot. Petrop. 5:36. 1839; Ledeb. Fl. Ross. 4:97. 1853; Maxim. in Bull. Acad. Sci. St. Petersb. 26:521. 1880; Dykes, Gen. Iris 73. 1913. p.p.; Makino et Nemoto, Fl. Jap. ed. 2, 1592. 1931; B. Fedtsch. in Kom. Fl. URSS 4:524. 1935; Liu Yin, Chinese Magazine of Botany 3 (2):943. 1936; Kitagawa, Lineam. Fl. Mansh. 148. 1939; Saragawa, Ill. Fl. Saghal. 599. 1939; Ohwi, Fl. Jap. 333. 1956.

Perennial herb, stem base with maroon-brown fibrous and hairlike remains of old leaves. Rhizome thick and strong, creeping, maroon-brown, about 1 cm in diameter; roots yellowish white, with wrinkled transverse patterns. Leaves grayish green, sword shaped or broadly strap shaped, 40 to 100 cm long, 0.8 to 1.5 cm wide, apex acuminate, base sheathlike, without obvious midribs. Flower stem solid, glossy, 40 to 60 cm high, with two to three leaflets in middle and lower parts; bracts 3 to 5, membranous, lanceolate, 6 to 9 cm long, 1 to 1.5 cm wide, apex acuminate or short-acuminate, midrib obvious; containing two to four flowers; flowers large, violet, 9 to 10 cm in diameter; pedicel 1.5 to 3.5 cm long; perianth tube with upper part swollen, trumpet shaped, about 2 cm long, 5 to 7 mm in diameter; falls obovate or elliptical, 7.5 to 9 cm long, 4 to 4.5 cm wide, blades pendulous, hafts yellow without beard, standards erect, oblanceolate, 5 to 6.5 cm long, 0.8 to 1.5 cm wide; stamens about 3 cm long, anthers white; style arms flat, petaloid, 5 to 6 cm long, 1.2 cm wide, crests semirounded, 1.5 to 2 cm long, margin undulate, ovary obtuse-triangular to cylindrical, with upper part slightly swollen, about 2 to 2.2 cm long, about 6 mm in diameter. Capsule elliptical-cylindrical, 6.5 to 7 cm long, 2 to 2.5 cm in diameter, with three of six ridges relatively prominent; seed flat, semirounded, brown, glossy, about 6.5 mm long, about 5 mm wide. Flowering in May to June, fruiting in July to August.

Native to Heilongjiang, Jilin, Liaoning, and Yunnan. Grows

along damp sides of pond and stream banks, in Yunnan at damp sites at an altitude of 1890 to 3200 m. Also native to Japan, Korea, and Russia.

12. Ussuri River Iris Plate F:1

Iris maackii Maxim. in Bull. Acad. Sci. St. Petersb. 26:542. 1880; Kom. Fl. Mansh. 418. 1927; V. N. Voloshilov, Fl. Soviet Far East 127–128. 1966; Defining Larger Plants of the Sakhalin and Kurile Islands 121. 1974;—*I. pseudacorus* auct. non. L.: Regel, Tent. Fl. Ussuri 148. 1861;—*I. pseudacorus* L. var. *manshurica* Hort.: Bailey, Man. Cult. Pl. 273. 1949;—*I. laevigata* auct. non Fisch.: O. Fedtsch. Kneucker's Allgemeine Botanishe Zeitschrift 6.1906.

Perennial herb. Rhizome thick and large, creeping. Leaves grayish green, sword shaped, 20 to 45 cm long, 0.7 to 1.5 cm wide, apex acuminate, base sheathlike and surrounding stem, midrib not obvious. Flower stem cylindrical, taller than 80 cm, 6 to 8 mm in diameter, upper part with several slender branches, each branch with two or three leaflets, bracts membranous, green, lanceolate or narrow-ovate, 4.5 to 5.5 cm long, 1.5 cm wide, midrib obvious; containing one or two flowers; flowers yellow, 5 to 5.5 cm in diameter; pedicel 1 to 3 cm long; perianth tube about 1 cm long; falls obovate, about 4 cm long, about 1 cm wide, blade pendulous, without beard; standards erect, narrowly oblanceolate, about 2.5 cm long, about 4 mm wide; stamens about 2.5 cm long, anthers yellow; style arms about 3 cm long, crests obtuse deltoid, ovary narrowly spindle shaped, about 2.5 cm long, about 2 mm in diameter. Capsule pendulous, cylindrical-elliptical, 6 to 9 cm long, 1.5 to 1.8 cm in diameter, base rounded, apex with short conical points, six thin ribs projecting and obvious. Seed flat, maroon-brown, surface with small projecting bumps, about 7 mm long, about 5 mm wide. Flowering in May, fruiting in June to August.

Native to Heilongjiang and Liaoning. Grows in damp sites near ponds and lakes. Also native to Russia. Type specimen from the estuary of the Iman River, the west bank of the Ussuri River.

13. Yellow-Flag Iris (Latin-Chinese Seed Plant Names) Yellow Iris (Handbook of Cultivated Plants of the Lushan Botanical Garden) Plate F:2

Iris pseudacorus L. Sp. Pl. 38. 1753; Dykes, Gen. Iris 76. 1913; B. Fedtsch. in Kom. Fl. URSS 4. 525. 1935.

Perennial herb, stem base with a few fibrous remains of old leaves. Rhizome large and thick up to 2.5 cm in diameter, creeping, yellowish brown; roots yellowish white, with wrinkled transverse

patterns. Basal leaves grayish green, broadly sword shaped, 40 to 60 cm long, 1.5 to 3 cm wide, apex acuminate, bases sheathlike, pale green, midrib relatively obvious. Flower stem large and thick with obvious ridges, 60 to 70 cm high, 4 to 6 mm in diameter, upper part branched; leaflets are shorter and narrower than basal leaves; bracts three or four, membranous, green, lanceolate, 6.5 to 8.5 cm long, 1.5 to 2 cm wide, apex acuminate; flowers yellow, 10 to 11 cm in diameter; pedicel 5 to 5.5 cm long; perianth tube 1.5 cm long, falls ovate-orbicular or obovate, about 7 cm long, 4.5 to 5 cm wide with maroon-brown striped pattern; standards relatively small, oblanceolate, erect, 2.7 cm long, 5 mm wide; stamens about 3 cm long, filaments yellowish white, anthers dark purple; style arms pale yellow, about 4.5 cm long, 1.2 cm wide, crests semirounded, margin slightly toothed, ovary green, three edged cylindrical, about 2.5 cm long, about 5 mm in diameter. Flowering in May, fruiting in June to August.

Native to Europe, cultivated in China. Grows well in damp sites near lakesides or ponds. Type specimen from Europe.

14. Varied-Color Iris

Iris versicolor L. Sp. Pl. 39. 1753; Williams in Curtis's Bot. Mag. t. 21. 1787; Baker in Journ. L. Soc. 16:141. 1878; Dykes, Gen. Iris 79. 1913; Bailey, Man. Cult. Pl. 272. 1949.

Perennial herb, stem base with a few fibrous remains of old leaves. Rhizome cylindrical, creeping, with maroon-brown old leaves which persist as fibers. Leaves slightly glaucous, sword shaped, 40 to 60 cm long, 1.3 to 1.8 cm wide, without obvious midrib. Flower stem 45 to 60 cm high, about 6 mm in diameter, upper part with two or three branches, branches 10 to 14 cm long; bracts three or four, lanceolate or narrowly lanceolate, 4 to 8 cm long, margin membranous, containing two or three flowers; flowers violet, 8 to 9 cm in diameter; perianth tube 0.5 to 1 cm long, falls oblanceolate, 6 to 7 cm long, 1 to 1.5 cm wide, without beard, standards oblanceolate and relatively shorter and smaller than falls, about 3 cm long, erect; stamens about 5 cm long, anthers violet; style arms 6 cm long, violet, crests semirounded, ovary three edged cylindrical. Capsule three edged cylindrical, 4 to 5 cm long, apex obtuse,

PLATE F   1. **Ussuri Iris** *Iris maackii* Maxim.: Upper stem with flowering branch.
2. **Yellow-Flag Iris** *Iris pseudacorus* L.: Flowering branch.
3. **Small Yellow-Flowered Iris** *Iris minutoaurea* Makino: Plant.
4. **Long-Tail Iris** *Iris rossii* Baker: Plant.
DRAWN BY YU ZHEN-ZHOU AND ZHAO YU-TANG

without points. Flowering in May, fruiting in June to September.
Native to America, cultivated in many places in China. Type
specimen from North America.

15. **Small Yellow-Flowered Iris** Plate F:3

Iris minutoaurea Makino in Journ. Jap. Bot. 5:17. 1928; Makino et
Nemoto, Fl. Jap. ed. 2, 1592. 1931;—*I. minuta* Franch. et Sav.
Enum. Pl. Jap. 2:42. 521. 1879 non Linn. f. 1781; Maxim. in Bull.
Acad. Sci. St. Petersb. 26:523. 1880; Makino in Bot. Mag. Tokyo
16:148. 1902; Stapf in Curtis's Bot. Mag. t. 8293. 1910; Dykes,
Gen. Iris 48. 1913;—*I. koreana* auct. non Nakai; Kitagawa,
Lineam. Fl. Mansh. 147. 1939.

Perennial herb, stem base with yellowish brown or maroon
sheaths of old leaves which persist as fibers. Rhizome long and
thin, filiform, yellowish brown, with many branched hairy roots.
Leaves narrow, strap shaped, 5 to 16 cm long, 2 to 7 mm wide, apex
acuminate, with three to five fine veins, without obvious midrib.
Flower stem slender, 7 to 15 cm; bracts two, membranous, lanceolate, 4 to 5 cm long, 5 to 10 mm wide, apex acuminate or short
acuminate, midrib obvious, containing one flower; flowers yellow,
2.5 to 3 cm in diameter; pedicel slender, 1.5 to 2 cm; perianth tube
filiform, apex swollen, 1.5 to 2 cm long, falls obovate, about 2.2 cm
long, about 8 mm wide, without beard, standards erect, oblanceolate, about 1.5 cm long, 3 to 4 mm wide, apex obtuse, retuse;
stamens about 1 cm long, anthers yellowish brown; style arms flat,
about 1.5 cm long, about 3 mm wide, crests elongate-deltoid, edged
with a few teeth, ovary spindle shaped, about 1 cm long, about 2 to
3 mm in diameter. Capsule almost globular. Flowering in May,
fruiting in June to July.

Native to southeast Liaoning. Grows among grass on hillsides
and at forest edges. Also native to Japan. Type specimen from
Japan.

16. **Long-Tailed Iris** (Key to Northeast Plants) Ross Iris (Key to the
Flora of Northeast China) Plate F:4

Iris rossii Baker in Gard. Chron. 3:809. 1877; Maxim. in Bull. Acad.
Sci. St. Petersb. 26:523. 1880; Dykes, Gen. Iris 48. 1913; Kom.
Fl. Mansh. 418. 1927; Liu Yin, Chinese Magazine of Botany
3(2):951. 1936; Kitagawa, Lineam. Fl. Mansh. 148. 1939; Ohwi,
Fl. Jap. 332. 1956; Key to Northeast China Plants 586. 1959.

Perennial herb, stem base with yellowish brown persistent sheaths
and fibers of old leaves. Rhizome relatively thick, not filiform,
**creeping, tough, with many nodes, reddish maroon; roots hairy,
thin, long, and tough, reddish maroon. Leaves strap shaped or**

narrowly linear, 4 to 10 (15) cm long, 2 to 5 mm wide, apex long-acuminate, with two to four thin ribs. Flower stem very short, barely emerging from the ground, base with two or three narrowly linear or narrowly lanceolate leaves; bracts two, narrowly lanceolate, 4 to 7 cm long, 5 to 8 mm wide, apex long-acuminate or long-caudate, containing one flower; flowers violet, 3.5 to 4 cm in diameter; pedicel about 1 cm long; perianth tube slender, 5 to 7 cm long, falls obovate, about 3 cm long, 0.8 to 1.2 cm wide, without beard, standards obovate or broad oblanceolate, about 2.5 cm long, about 8 mm wide, erect or inclined outward; stamens about 1.5 cm; anthers shorter than filaments; style arms flat, about 2 cm long, crests narrowly deltoid, ovary spindle shaped, about 1 cm long. Capsule globular. Flowering in April to May, fruiting June to August.

Native to southern Liaoning. Grows on sunny hillsides and meadows at forest edges. Also native to Japan and Korea. Type specimen from northeast China.

Native only to Funghuang Shan Mountain area in Liaoning, not native to southern China. Several literature references confuse this with Small Iris (*Iris proantha*) and Larger Small Iris (*Iris proantha* var. *valida*) which are native to mid-China and eastern China.

17. **Long-Pedicel Iris** Plate G:1

Iris henryi Baker, Handb. Irid. 6. 1892; Dykes, Gen. Iris 49. 1913; Liu Yin, Chinese Magazine of Botany 3(2):591. 1936;—*I. gracilipes* Pampan. in Nuov. Giorn. Bot. Ital. 22:269. 1915.

Perennial sparsely tufted herb, stem base slightly reddish purple, with old leaves which persist as fibers. Rhizome slender, creeping, maroon-brown; roots slender. Leaves pale green, narrowly strap shaped, 15 to 40 cm long, about 2 mm wide, apex acuminate, with one or two thin veins. Flower stem thin, 15 to 25 cm high, base with one or two leaves; bracts two or three, green, narrowly lanceolate, 3 to 4 cm long, apex acuminate, with two flowers; flowers blue or violet, 2.5 to 3 cm in diameter; pedicel slender, 2 to 4 cm long; perianth tube relatively short, trumpet shaped, 3 to 5 mm long without a beard; falls obovate, about 2 cm long, about 7 mm wide, lower part mottled yellow, standards similar to falls but relatively smaller; stamens about 1 cm long, anthers strap shaped; style arms flat, petaloid, about 1 cm long, crests narrowly deltoid, ovary green, narrowly spindle shaped, 5 to 7 mm long. Flowering in May, fruiting in June to August.

Native to Hunan, Hubei, and Sichuan. Grows among grass in

forest or at forest edges. Type specimen from the bank of the Yangtze River, western Hubei.

18. **Mountain Iris** (Key to the Flora of Northeast China) Plate G:2–4

Iris setosa Pall. ex Link in Engl. Bot. Jahrb. 1(3):71. 1820; Baker in Journ. Linn. Soc. 16:140. 1878; Maxim. in Bull. Acad. Sci. St. Petersb. 26:522. 1880; Dykes, Gen. Iris 92, pl. 23. 1913; Kom. Fl. Mansh. 416. 1927; B. Fedtsch. in Kom. Fl. URSS 4:520. 1935; Kitagawa, Lineam. Fl. Mansh. 149. 1939; Shigezo Saragawa, Ill. Fl. Saghal. 2:599. 1939; Ohwi, Fl. Jap. 333. 1956.

Perennial herb, stem base with maroon-brown old leaves which persist as fibers. Rhizome thick, creeping, grayish brown; roots cordlike, yellowish white. Leaves sword shaped or broadly linear, 30 to 60 cm long, 0.8 to 1.8 cm wide, apex acuminate, base sheathlike, without obvious midribs. Flower stem glabrous, 60 to 100 cm high, upper part with one to three thin long branches, with one to three leaflets; each branch with three bracts, membranous, green tinted slightly reddish brown, lanceolate to ovate-orbicular, 2 to 4 cm long, 0.8 to 1.6 cm wide, apex acuminate; flowers violet, 7 to 8 cm in diameter; pedicel thin, 2.5 to 3.5 cm long; perianth tube short, trumpet shaped, about 1 cm long, falls broadly obovate, 4 to 4.5 cm long, 2 to 2.5 cm wide, blades pendulous, hafts of falls cuneiform, yellow with purple-striped pattern, without a beard; standards short and narrowly lanceolate, about 2.5 cm long, about 5 mm wide, erect; stamens about 2 cm long, anthers purple, filaments the same length as anthers, style arms flat, about 3 cm long, 1.6 to 2 cm wide, crests almost square, margins slightly toothed, ovary cylindrical, about 1 cm long. Capsule elliptical to ovate-orbicular, about 3 cm long, 1.8 to 2 cm in diameter, apex without points, six obvious projecting ribs; seed pale brown. Flowering in July, fruiting in August to September.

Native to Jilin. Grows between the altitudes of 1500 to 2500 m in wet subalpine meadows or near ponds. Also native to Japan, Korea, Russia, and North America. Type specimen from east Siberia, Russia.

PLATE G   1. **Long-Pedicel Iris** *Iris henryi* Baker: Plant.
2–4. **Mountain Iris** *Iris setosa* Pall. ex Link: 2. Lower part of stem with rhizome. 3. Upper stem with flowering branch. 4. Fruiting branch.
DRAWN BY YU ZHEN-ZHOU AND ZHAO YU-TANG

19. White-Flowered Chinese Iris

Iris lactea Pall. Reise Russ. Reich. 3:713. 1776; Kitagawa in Rep.
Inst. Sci. Res. Mansh. 4:114. 1940.

Perennial herb. Rhizome thick, woody, creeping, sheathed with
many dense reddish purple old leaves which persist as hairy fibers;
roots thick and long, yellowish white, with few branches. Leaves
basal, grayish green, linear or narrow sword shaped, 50 cm long, 4
to 6 mm wide, apex acuminate, base sheathlike, slightly reddish
purple, without obvious midribs. Flower stem glabrous, 3 to 10 cm
high; bracts three to five, green, margins white, lanceolate, 4.5 to 10
cm long, 0.8 to 1.6 cm wide, apex acuminate or long-acuminate,
containing two to four flowers; flower milky white, 5 to 6 cm in
diameter; pedicel 4 to 7 cm long; perianth tube very short, about 3
mm long, falls oblanceolate, 4.5 to 6.5 cm long, 0.8 to 1.2 cm wide,
apex obtuse or mucronate, hafts of fall cuneiform; standards
narrowly oblanceolate, 4.2 to 4.5 cm long, 5 to 7 mm wide; stamens
2.5 to 3.2 cm long, anthers yellow, filaments white; ovary spindlelike, 3 to 4.5 cm long. Capsule long elliptical-columnar, 4 to 6 cm
long, 1 to 1.4 cm in diameter, with six obvious ribs, apex with short
point; seed irregular polyhedron, maroon-brown, slightly glossy.
Flowering in May to June, fruiting from June to September.

Native to Jilin, Inner Mongolia, Qinghai, Xinjiang, and Tibet.
Grows in uncultivated places, along roadsides, and among grasses
on hillsides.

19a. **Chinese Iris** (Illustrated Classics of Medicinal Plants) Wooden
Dipper Fruit (Shen Nung's Classic Medicinal Plants) Violet
Grass, Blue-Flower Grass (Anhui), Wind of Arrow Shaft,
Horse Broom (Hunan), Horse Lotus (North, Northwest and
Northeast China) Plate H:1–2

var. *chinensis* (Fisch.) Koidz. in Bot. Mag. Tokyo. 39:300. 1925;
Makino et Nemoto, Fl. Jap. ed. 2, 1591. 1931: Flora of Beijing
(Monocots) 302, Fig. 330. 1975; Flora of Qin Ling 1(1):387.
1976;—*I. pallasii* Fisch. var. *chinensis* Fisch. in Curtis's Bot. Mag.
t. 2331. 1822;—*I. ensata* auct. non Thunb.: Maxim. in Bull. Acad.
Sci. St. Petersb. 26:521. 1880; Hook. f. Fl. Brit. Ind. 6:272. 1892;
C. H. Wright in Journ. Linn. Soc. Bot. 36:81. 1903; Dykes, Gen.
Iris 85. 1913; B. Fedtsch. in Kom. Fl. URSS 4:518. 1935; Liu Yin,
Chinese Magazine of Botany 3(2):944. 1936; Iconographia
Cormophytorum Sinicorum 5:579, Fig. 7987. 1976;—*I.
longispatha* Fisch. in Curtis's Bot. Mag. t. 2528. 1825;—*I. biglumis*
Vahl. Enum. 3:149. 1806;—*I. enstata* Thunb. var. *chinensis*
Maxim. Gartenfl. 161, t. 1011. 1880, et in Bull. Acad. Sci. St.

Petersb. 26:514. 1880; Kom. Fl. Mansh. 2:409. 1927;—*I. illiensis* P. Pol. in Notul. Syst. Herb. Acad. Sci. URSS 12:88. 1950. Flower pale blue, blue or violet, perianth with relatively deeply colored, veined pattern.

Native to Heilongjiang, Jilin, Liaoning, Inner Mongolia, Hebei, Shandong, Shanxi, Henan, Anhui, Jiangsu, Zhejiang, Hubei, Hunan, Shaanxi, Gansu, Ningxia, Qinghai, Xinjiang, Sichuan, and Tibet. Grows in uncultivated places, along roadsides, among grass on hillsides especially on overgrazed grasslands. Also native to Korea, Russia, and India.

This plant is resistant to high concentrations of salt and alkaline soils, it can tolerate trampling underfoot, and it improves the soil texture. Root system well developed; leaves persistent during winter and can be used as feed for cattle, sheep, and camels; also can be used for making paper; xylem fibers of root tough, fine grained and long, can be used to make brushes; flowers and seeds are used medicinally, seed can be used in the preparation of an herbal contraceptive.

19b. Yellow-Flowered Chinese Iris
var. *chrysantha* Y. T. Zhao, Pub. of Coll. of Plant. Res., Lab. of Northeast Forestry Inst. 9. 76. 1980.

Flower yellow, other characters the same as those of *Iris lactea*.

Native to Tibet. Type specimen from Nierong County, Tibet.

20. Slender-Leaf Iris (Key to Northeast Plants) Old Cow Pull, Slender-Leaf Chinese Iris, Thread-Leaf Chinese Iris (Northeast China) Plate H:3–4
Iris tenuifolia Pall. Reise. Russ. Reich. 3:714, t. c. f. 2. 1776; Ledeb. Fl. Alt. 1:55. 1829, et. Fl. Ross. 4:93. 1853; Baker in Gard. Chron. ser. 2, 6:144. 1876; Maxim. in Bull. Acad. Sci. St. Petersb. 26:511. 1880; C. H. Wright in Journ. Linn. Soc. Bot. 36:85. 1903; Dykes, Gen. Iris 32. 1913; B. Fedtsch. in Kom. Fl. URSS 4:515. 1935; Liu Yin, Chinese Magazine of Botany 3(2):949. 1936; Kitagawa, Lineam. Fl. Mansh. 149. 1939; Key to Northeast Plants 586 Pl. 220:4. 1959; Iconographia Cormophytorum Sinicorum 5:578, Fig. 7986. 1976.

Perennial densely tufted herb, stem base with persistent reddish brown or yellowish maroon old leaf sheaths, rhizome knobby, short and hard, woody, black-brown; roots tough and hard, branches few. Leaves filiform or very narrowly linear, 20 to 60 cm long, 1.5 to 2 mm wide, twisted, without obvious midribs. Flower stem usually very short, not emerging from the ground; bracts four, lanceolate, 5 to 10 cm long, 8 to 10 mm wide, apex long-

acuminate or caudate-acuminate, margin membranous, with obvious midribs, containing two or three flowers; flowers violet, about 7 cm in diameter; pedicel thin, 3 to 4 mm long; perianth tube 4.5 to 6 cm long, falls spatulate, 4.5 to 5 cm long, about 1.5 cm wide, hafts of fall long and narrowly linear without beard on midrib, but always with a few cilia, standards oblanceolate, about 5 cm long, about 5 mm wide, erect; stamens about 3 cm long, filaments and anthers almost the same length; style arms about 4 cm long, 4 to 5 mm wide, crests narrowly deltoid, ovary slender cylindrical, 0.7 to 1.2 cm long, about 2 mm in diameter. Capsule obovate, 3.2 to 4.5 cm long, 1.2 to 1.8 cm in diameter, apex with short point, at ripening, capsules split open from tip to base. Flowering in April to May, fruiting in August to September.

Native to Heilongjiang, Jilin, Liaoning, Inner Mongolia, Hebei, Shanxi, Shaanxi, Gansu, Ningxia, Qinghai, Xinjiang, and Tibet. Grows in fixed dunes or on sandy soil. Also native to Russia, Mongolia, Afghanistan, and Turkey.

Leaves can be used to make rope or other fibers.

21. **Tiny Iris** (Key to Northeast Plants) Plate H:5

Iris kobayashii Kitagawa in Journ. Jap. Bot. 9 (4):294–295. 1933, et Lineam. Fl. Mansh. 147. 1939; Key to Northeast Plants 586. 1959.

Perennial herb, stem base with persistent old leaf sheaths, yellowish brown or maroon-purple. Rhizome knobby, short and rough, woody, maroon-brown; roots hairy yellowish maroon, with few branches. Leaves slightly twisted, narrowly linear, 10 to 20 cm long, about 3 mm wide, apex acuminate, without obvious midrib. Flower stem short, generally not emerging from the ground; bracts two or three, green, narrowly lanceolate, 6 to 8 cm long, 0.8 to 1 cm wide, apex long-acuminate, containing one or two flowers; flowers blue with yellow markings, about 3 cm in diameter; pedicel relatively short, about 1.5 cm long; perianth tube slender, 4 to 5 cm long, falls narrowly oblanceolate, about 3 cm long, about 5 mm wide, blade angled outward, standards narrowly oblanceolate, about 2 cm long, 2 to 3 mm wide, erect; stamens 1.5 to 1.8 cm long, anthers yellow or yellowish brown; style arms shorter and narrower than petals, crests narrowly deltoid, filiform, ovary

PLATE H 1–2. **Chinese Iris** *Iris lactea* Pall. var. *chinensis* (Fisch.) Koidz.: 1. Plant with rhizome. 2. Fruiting branch.
3–4. **Slender-Leaf Iris** *Iris tenuifolia* Pall.: 3. Plant. 4. Capsule.
5. **Tiny Iris** *Iris kobayashii* Kitagawa: Plant.
DRAWN BY YU ZHEN-ZHOU AND ZHAO YU-TANG

narrowly cylindrical, about 1 cm long. Capsule long-orbicular, about 2 cm long, 7 to 8 mm in diameter, with six projecting ribs, apex with a short point. Flowering in May, fruiting in June to August.

Native to southern Liaoning. Grows on dry hillsides. Type specimen from Nanguanling near Dalien, Liaoning.

22. Qinghai Iris Plate I:1

Iris qinghainica Y. T. Zhao, Acta Phytotaxonomica Sinica 18 (1):55. 1980.

Perennial herb, stem base with persistent old leaf fibers, maroon-brown. Rhizome knobby; roots cordlike. Leaves grayish green, narrowly linear, 5 to 15 cm long, 2 to 3 mm wide, apex acuminate, without obvious midrib. Flower stem very short, not emerging from the ground, base always with lanceolate membranous sheath-like leaves; bracts three, green, margin membranous, pale green, lanceolate, 6 to 10 cm long, 6 to 18 mm wide, containing one or two flowers, flowers violet or blue, 4.5 to 5 cm in diameter; perianth tube filiform, 4 to 6 cm long, falls narrowly oblanceolate, 3 to 3.5 cm long, about 5 mm wide, blade angled outward, standards narrowly oblanceolate to linear, 3 cm long, about 4 mm wide, erect; stamens 1.8 to 2 cm long; style arms about 2.5 cm long, about 3 mm wide, crests narrowly lanceolate-deltoid, ovary thin cylindrical, middle part slightly thickened, about 1.5 cm long. Flowering in June to July, fruiting in July to August.

Native to Qinghai. Grows at an altitude of over 2500 m on high mountain hillsides and sunny grasslands. Type specimen from shore of Lake Qinghai.

23. Cathay Iris (Flora of Jiangsu) Plate I:2

Iris cathayensis Migo in Jour. Shanghai Sci. Inst. sect. 3. 4:140. 1939; Flora of Jiangsu, First Volume 395, Fig. 712. 1977.

Perennial herb, stem base with maroon-red old leaf sheaths. Rhizome knobby and woody; roots thick, upper and lower parts of equal thickness, maroon-brown or yellowish brown, with transverse patterns. Leaves basal, thin, grayish green, linear, at flowering 15 to 25 cm long, 3 to 4 mm wide, at fruiting up to 45 cm

PLATE I 1. **Qinghai Iris** *Iris qinghainica* Y. T. Zhao: Plant.
2. **Cathay Iris** *Iris cathayensis* Migo: Plant.
3–4. **Tian Shan Mountain Iris** *Iris loczyi* Kanitz: 3. Plant. 4. Part of a fruiting branch.
5–6. **Songar Iris** *Iris songarica* Schrenk: 5. Plant. 6. Fruiting branch.
DRAWN BY YU ZHEN-ZHOU

long, 6 mm wide, apex long-acuminate, pendulous, base sheath-like, without obvious midrib. Flower stem not emerging from the ground; bracts three or four, green, margin membranous, somewhat pale, lanceolate, 8 to 12 cm long, 1.2 to 2 cm wide, apex acuminate, midrib obvious, with two flowers; flowers violet, 6 to 7.5 cm in diameter; pedicel filiform, 1.5 to 2 cm long; perianth tube slender, apex somewhat swollen, 7 to 9 cm long, falls narrowly oblanceolate, 4 to 5.5 cm long, about 5 mm wide, standards narrowly oblanceolate 4 to 5 cm long, hafts linear, midrib with a few unicellular cilia; stamens 2.8 to 3.5 cm long, anthers blue longer than filaments; style arms linear, 3.5 to 4 cm long, about 3 mm wide, crests elongate linear, about 1.2 cm long, ovary spindle shaped, 1.3 to 1.5 cm long. Flowering in April.

Native to Anhui, Jiangsu, and Hubei. Grows on open hillsides and grasslands. Type specimen from Chulin Temple in Zhenjiang, Jiangsu.

24. Tianshan Mountain Iris Plate I:3–4

Iris loczyi Kanitz, Bot. Res. Szech. Cent. As. Exped. 58, t. 6, f. 2. 1891; S. K. Czerepanov, Addit. Corr. Fl. URSS 298. 1973;—*I. thianshanica* (Maxim.) Vved. in B. Fedtsch. Fl. Turkm. 1:325. 1932; B. Fedtsch. in Kom. Fl. URSS 4:515. 1935;—*I. tenuifolia* Pall. var. *thianschanica* Maxim. in Bull. Acad. Sci. St. Petersb. 26:511. 1880; R. Rol. Fl. Kazakh. 2:237. 1958;—*I. tenuifolia* auct. non. Pall.; Dykes, Gen. Iris 32. 1913.

Perennial densely tufted herb, old leaf sheaths persistent on rhizome, maroon or maroon-brown. Rhizome knobby, woody, dark maroon-brown. Leaves tough, erect, narrowly linear, 20 to 40 cm long, about 3 mm wide, apex acuminate, base sheathlike, without obvious midrib. Flower stem relatively short, not emerging or only slightly emerging from the ground, base always with lanceolate membranous sheathlike leaves; bracts three, 10 to 15 cm long, about 1.5 cm wide, midrib obvious, apex acuminate, containing one or two flowers; flower violet, 5.5 to 7 cm in diameter; perianth tube very long, filiform, up to 10 cm long, falls oblanceolate or narrowly obovate, 6 cm long, 1 to 2 cm wide, standards oblanceolate, 4.5 to 5 cm long, 7 to 8 mm wide; stamens about 2.5 cm long; style arms about 4 cm long, about 8 mm wide, crests semirounded, ovary spindlelike, about 1.2 cm long. Capsule long obovate to cylindrical, 4 to 7 cm long, about 2 cm in diameter, apex with slight short point, with six veins obvious, reddish brown when fresh, bract persistent on base of fruit. Flowering in May to June, fruiting in July to September.

Native to Inner Mongolia, Gansu, Ningxia, Qinghai, Xinjiang, Sichuan, and Tibet. Grows at an altitude above 2000 m in high mountains and sunny grasslands. Also native to Russia. Type specimen from Western Tianshan, Russia.

25. Many-Spotted Iris
Iris polysticta Diels in Svensk Bot. Tidskr. 18:428. 1924.
Perennial densely tufted herb, stem base with persistent old leaf sheaths, reddish maroon. Rhizome knobby and woody. Roots pale yellow. Leaves grayish green, linear or narrowly swordlike, 35 to 70 cm long, 4 to 7 mm wide, apex acuminate, base sheathlike, reddish purple, without obvious midribs. Flower stem 30 to 35 cm high, about 7 mm in diameter, yellowish green, with some edges, with one or two leaflets; bracts three, green, margin membranous, lanceolate, 13 to 20 cm long, 1.6 to 2.5 cm wide, apex acuminate; flowers yellow, with purple-brown netted patterns, 8 to 9 cm in diameter; pedicel 7 to 9 cm long; perianth tube short and thick, 3 to 5 mm long, 5 to 6 mm in diameter, falls pandurate, about 6.5 cm long, about 1.2 cm wide, apex obovate, hafts of falls lanceolate, standards oblanceolate, about 4.5 cm long, about 8 mm wide, erect; anthers pale red, about 3 cm long; style arms petaloid, yellow, 3.5 to 4 cm long, flat, crests semirounded. Capsule 3.5 to 7 cm long, about 1.6 cm in diameter. Flowering in June to July, fruiting in July to September.

Native to Sichuan, Yunnan, and Tibet. Grows in damp sites near riversides and on sunny banks. Type specimen from Songpan, Sichuan.

According to records, one other species, Grass-Leaf Iris (*Iris farreri* Dykes) is native to Yunnan. Its vegetative parts and characters are similar to *Iris polysticta*, but with grayish white flowers. Although I have not seen the type specimen, I include it here pending further study.

26. Songar Iris Plate I:5–6
Iris songarica Schrenk in Fisch. et Mey. Enum. Pl. Nov. 1:3. 1841; Ledeb. Fl. Ross. 4:99. 1853; Dykes, Gen. Iris 71. 1913; B. Fedtsch. in Kom. Fl. URSS 4:516. 1945; Liu Yin, Chinese Magazine of Botany 3(2):943. 1936;—*I. songarica* Schrenk var. *gracilis* Maxim. in Bull. Acad. Sci. St. Petersb. 26:510. 1880.
Perennial densely tufted herb, stem base with maroon-brown old leaf sheaths. Rhizome knobby, woody, maroon black; roots maroon brown, upper and lower parts of equal thickness. Leaves grayish green, linear, with three to five vertical veins, shorter than stem at flowering time, 15 to 23 cm long, 2 to 3 mm wide, elongating to 70

to 80 cm long, 0.7 to 1 cm wide at fruiting. Flower stem 25 to 50 cm high, glabrous, with three or four leaflets; bracts three, green, margin membranous, relatively pale, 7 to 14 cm long, 1.8 to 2 cm wide, apex short-acuminate, containing two flowers; pedicel 4.5 cm long; flowers violet, 8 to 9 cm in diameter; perianth tube 5 to 7 mm long, falls pandurate, 5 to 5.5 cm long, about 1 cm wide, blade elliptical or ovate-orbicular, hafts nearly lanceolate, standards oblanceolate, about 3.5 cm long, about 5 mm wide, erect; stamens about 2.5 cm long, anthers brown; style arms about 3.5 cm long, about 1 cm wide, crests narrowly deltoid, ovary spindlelike, about 2.5 cm long. Capsule three ridged ovate-orbicular, 4 to 6.5 cm long, 1.5 to 2 cm in diameter, apex with long point, pericarp coriaceous, with obvious network of veins; at ripening the capsule splits down one-third from the top, seeds maroon-brown, pomoid, without aril, surface somewhat wrinkled. Flowering in June to July, fruiting in August to September.

Native to Shaanxi, Gansu, Ningxia, Qinghai, Xinjiang, and Sichuan. Grows in sunny high mountain grasslands, banks, and stony hillsides. Also native to Russia, Iran, Turkey, Afghanistan, and Pakistan. Type specimen from the Songar Basin, Xinjiang.

27. Large Bract Iris Plate J:1–2

Iris bungei Maxim. in Bull. Acad. Sci. St. Petersb. 26:509. 1880; C. H. Wright in Journ. Linn. Soc. Bot. 36:80. 1903; Dykes, Gen. Iris 34. 1913; Liu Yin, Chinese Magazine of Botany 3(2):950. 1936.

Perennial densely tufted herb, old leaf sheaths persisting at base, maroon-brown or light maroon, 10 to 13 cm long. Rhizome knobby, woody; roots long and thick, yellowish white or yellowish brown. Leaves linear, 20 to 50 cm long, 2 to 4 mm wide, with four to seven vertical veins, without obvious midrib. Flower stem height often variable according to the soil depth, usually 15 to 25 cm high, with two to three leaves, leaf base sheathlike; bracts three, green, margin membranous, white, broadly ovate or ovate, 8 to 10 cm long, 3 to 4 cm wide, without transverse veins connecting between parallel veins, midrib obvious and raised, containing two flowers; flowers violet, 6 to 7 cm in diameter; pedicel about 1.5 cm long; perianth tube filiform, 6 to 7 cm long; falls 5 to 6 cm long, 1.2 to 1.5 cm wide, standards oblanceolate, 5 to 5.5 cm long, 0.8 to 1 cm wide, erect; stamens about 3 cm long; style arms 5 to 5.5 cm long, crests lanceolate-deltoid, ovary green, thin cylindrical, 4 to 4.5 cm long. Capsule narrowly cylindrical, ovate, 8 to 9 cm long, 1.5 to 2 cm in diameter, with six obvious veins, apex with point, at ripening the capsule splits down one-third from the top. Flowering in May to June, fruiting in July to August.

Native to Inner Mongolia, Shanxi, Gansu, and Ningxia. Grows in desert, semiwilderness, sandy grasslands, or dunes. Also native to Mongolia. Type specimen from Mongolia.

The length of this species' flower stem often depends on the soil depth. Either it does not emerge or it emerges only slightly from the ground. Bracts are wide and enlarged, without transverse veins crossing between the parallel veins. This characteristic distinguishes it from the Pouch Flower Iris, *Iris ventricosa*.

28. **Pouch-Flower Iris** (Key to Northeast Plants) Large-Bract Iris (Chinese Magazine of Botany) Plate J:3–6

Iris ventricosa Pall. Reise Russ. Reich. 3:712. 1776; Ledeb. Fl. Ross. 4:94. 1853; Baker in Gard. Chron. ser. 2, 6:143. 1876; Maxim. in Bull. Acad. Sci. St. Petersb. 26:509. 1880; Dykes, Gen. Iris 34. 1913; Kom. Fl. Mansh. 2:407. 1927; B. Fedtsch. in Kom. Fl. URSS 4:516. 1935; Liu Yin, Chinese Magazine of Botany 3(2):950. 1936; Kitagawa, Lineam. Fl. Mansh. 149. 1939; Key to Northeast Plants 586. 1959: Iconographia Cormophytorum Sinicorum 5:575, Fig. 7979. 1976.

Perennial herb, stem base with persistent light or dark brown sheathing of old leaves. Rhizome dense, woody, tuberlike; roots grayish yellow, tough, both upper and lower parts of equal thickness. Leaves linear, grayish green, 20 to 35 cm long, 3 to 4 mm wide, apex acuminate, with few veins, without obvious midrib. Flower stem 10 to 15 cm high, cylindrical, with one or two leaflets; bracts three, grassy, with membranous margin, ovate or wide lanceolate, 6 to 8 cm long, 2.5 to 4 cm wide, apex long-acuminate, with transverse veins linking each other and making a network between parallel veins; flowers violet, 6 to 7 cm in diameter; pedicel 1 to 1.5 cm long; perianth tube slender, filiform, 2.5 to 4 cm long, upper part slightly swollen, falls narrowly spoon shaped, 4.5 to 5 cm long, 0.8 to 1 cm wide, midrib rarely with a few unicellular thin hairs, but not a beard, standards widely linear or narrow lanceolate, 3.5 to 4 cm long, 7 to 8 mm wide; stamens 3 to 3.5 cm long, anthers yellowish purple; style arms flat, 3.5 to 3.8 cm long, about 6 mm wide, apex ribbonlike or narrowly deltoid, ovary cylindrical, middle part slightly swollen, 1.5 cm long, 2.5 to 3 mm in diameter. Capsule three ridged ovate-orbicular, 2.5 to 4 cm long, about 1 cm in diameter, base rounded, apex long acuminate, point 2 to 4.5 cm long, six obvious veins; at ripening the capsule splits one-third of the way down from the top.

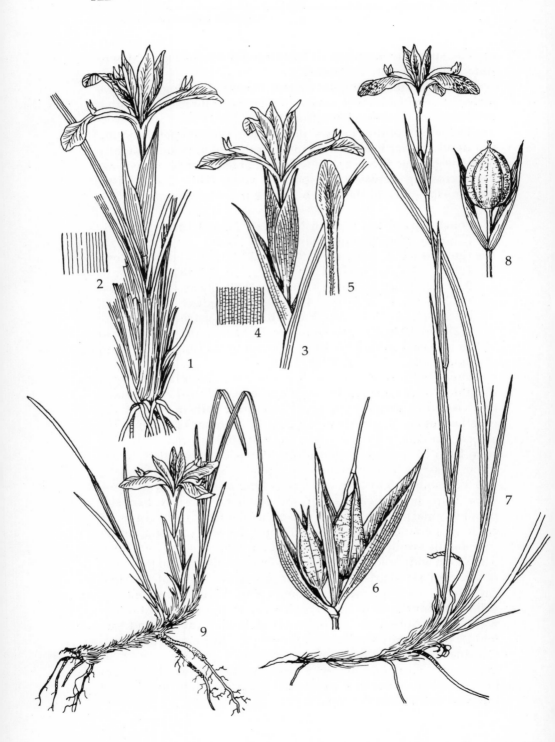

Native to Heilongjiang, Jilin, Liaoning, Inner Mongolia, and Hebei. Grows in dunes or sandy grasslands. Also native to Russia and Mongolia. Type specimen from the middle part of Siberia, Russia.

This species is similar to the Large-Bract Iris (*Iris bungei*), but in this species the bracts have transverse veins linking the parallel veins.

Section 2. Purple-Bract Iris Section—Sect. *Ioniris* Spach. in Ann. Sci. Nat. ser. 3, 5:98. 1846; em. Rodion. Genus Iris—*Iris* L. 190. 1961.

29. **Purple-Bract Iris** (Key to Northeast Plants) Russian Iris (Chinese Magazine of Botany) Purple Gladiolus (Emperor Qian Lung's Imperial Collection) Soviet Union Iris (Flora of Qin Ling) Slender-Stem Iris (Iconographia Cormophytorum Sinicorum) Plate J:7–8

Iris ruthenica Ker-Gawl. in Curtis's Bot. Mag. t. 1123. 1808, et t. 1393. 1811; Hance in Journ. Bot. 13:139. 1875; Baker in Journ. Linn. Soc. 16:138. 1878; Maxim. in Bull. Acad. Sci. St. Petersb. 26:516. 1880; Dykes, Gen. Iris 52, pl. 13. 1913. p. p. ; Iconographia Cormophytorum Sinicorum 5:579, Fig. 7988. 1976. p.p.

Perennial herb, stem base surrounded with short sheathlike leaves. Rhizome creeping, branched, nodes obvious, with maroon-brown old leaves which persist as fibers, 3 to 5 mm in diameter; roots thick, dark brown. Leaves linear, grayish green, 20 to 25 cm long, 3 to 6 mm wide, apex long acuminate, base sheathlike, with three to five parallel veins. Flower stem thin, 15 to 20 cm high, with two or three leaflets; bracts two, membranous, green, margined reddish purple, lanceolate or widely lanceolate, about 3 cm long, 0.8 to 1 cm wide, midrib obvious, containing one flower; flowers violet, 5 to 5.5 cm in diameter; pedicel 0.6 to 1 cm long; perianth tube 1 to 1.2 cm long, falls oblanceolate, about 4 cm long, 0.8 to 1 cm wide, with white and deep purple mottled patterns, standards

PLATE J   1–2. **Large-Bract Iris** *Iris bungei* Maxim.: 1. Plant. 2. Vein pattern on bract.
3–6. **Pouch-Flowered Iris** *Iris ventricosa* Pall.: 3. Flowering branch. 4. Vein pattern on bract. 5. Fall. 6. Fruiting branch.
7–8. **Purple-Bract Iris** *Iris ruthenica* Ker-Gawl.: 7. Plant. 8. Fruiting branch.
9. **Dwarf Purple-Bract Iris** *Iris ruthenica* Ker-Gawl. var. *nana* Maxim.: Plant.
DRAWN BY YU ZHEN-ZHOU

erect, narrowly oblanceolate, 3.2 to 3.5 cm long, about 6 mm wide; stamens about 2.5 cm long, anthers milky white; style arms flat, 3.5 to 4 cm long, crests narrowly deltoid, ovary narrowly spindle shaped, about 1 cm long. Capsule globular or ovate-orbicular, 1.2 to 1.5 cm in diameter, with six obvious midribs, apex without points; at ripening the capsule splits from apex about halfway down; seeds globular or pomoid, with milk-white aril, sticky when wet. Flowering in May to June, fruiting in July to August.

Native to Xinjiang. Grows in sunny grasslands or stony hillsides. Also native to Russia. Type specimen from a cultivated plant whose seeds were collected from Siberia, Russia, in 1804.

29a. Short Tube Purple-Bract Iris
var. *brevituba* Maxim. in Bull. Acad. Sci. St. Petersb. 26:516.
    1880;—*I. brevituba* (Maxim.) Vved. Fl. Kiriz. URSS 3:131. 1951.
This variety is distinguished from *Iris ruthenica* by the shorter perianth tube, which is usually 5 to 8 mm long (1 to 1.5 cm in *I. ruthenica*), other characteristics are similar to *Iris ruthenica*.

Native to Xinjiang. Also native to Russia.

29b. Dwarf Purple-Bract Iris Plate J:9
var. *nana* Maxim. in Bull. Acad. Sci. St. Petersb. 26:516. 1880;
    Makino et Nemoto, Fl. Jap. ed. 2, 1593. 1931.
This variety differs from *Iris ruthenica* by its shorter stem. Leaves 8 to 15 cm long, 1.5 to 3 mm wide. Flower stem 5 to 5.5 cm high; bract 1.5 to 3 cm long, 3 to 8 mm wide; flower pale blue or violet, 3.5 to 4.5 cm in diameter; perianth tube 1 to 1.5 cm long, falls about 2.5 cm long, about 6 mm wide, marked with lines or mottling, standards about 2 cm long; stamens about 1.5 cm long, ovary narrowly ovate, cylindrical, about 4 mm long. Flowering in April to May, fruiting in June to July.

Native to Heilongjiang, Jilin, Liaoning, Inner Mongolia, Hebei, Shanxi, Shandong, Henan, Jiangsu, Zhejiang, Shaanxi, Gansu, Ningxia, Sichuan, Yunnan, and Tibet. Grows in sunny sandy soil or on hillsides and grasslands.

29c. White-Flower Purple-Bract Iris
f. *leucantha* Y. T. Zhao Acta Phytotaxonomica Sinica 18(1):56.
    1980.
This form's vegetative characteristics and habit are similar to *Iris ruthenica*, but it is distinguished by its white flower.

Native to Xinjiang.

30. **Single-Flower Iris** (Key to Northeast Plants)
Iris uniflora Pall. ex Link in Engl. Bot. Jahrb. 1(3):71. 1820; Kom. Fl.
    Mansh. 409. 1927; Kitagawa, Lineam. Fl. Mansh. 149. 1939;—*I.*
    ruthenica Ker-Gawl. var. *uniflora* Baker, Handb. Irid. 4. 1892;—*I.*
    ruthenica auct. non. Ker-Gawl.: Dykes, Gen Iris 52. 1913. p. p.;
    B. Fedtsch. in Kom. Fl. URSS 4:518. 1935.
Perennial herb, stem base surrounded by yellowish brown old
leaves which persist as fibers and membranous sheathlike leaves.
Rhizome slender, creeping, branched, nodes slightly swollen,
maroon brown; roots thin. Leaves linear or lanceolate; at
flowering, leaves 5 to 20 cm long, 0.4 to 1 cm wide; at fruiting,
leaves up to 30 to 45 cm long, apex acuminate, base sheathlike,
without obvious midribs. Flower stem thin, lower half with one
membranous, lanceolate leaflet; bracts two, of same length, hard
and dry-membranous, yellowish green, with slightly reddish
margin, lanceolate or widely lanceolate, 2 to 3.5 cm long, 0.8 to 1 cm
wide; apex obtuse containing one flower; flowers violet, 4 to 4.5 cm
in diameter; pedicel very short; perianth tube thin, about 1.5 cm
long, upper part swollen and trumpet shaped; falls narrowly
oblanceolate, about 3 cm long, about 8 mm wide, blades ovate-
orbicular, standards linear or narrowly lanceolate, about 3 cm long,
about 3 mm wide, erect; stamens about 1.5 cm long, filaments
slender; style arms flat, about the same size as the standards, crests
almost semiorbicular, margin barely toothed; ovary cylindrical
spindle shaped, about 5 mm long. Capsule orbicular-globular, 0.8
to 1 cm in diameter, with six obvious ribs, with yellow
membranous bracts persistent at base. Flowering in May to June,
fruiting in July to August.
    Native to Heilongjiang, Jilin, Liaoning, and Inner Mongolia.
Grows on hillsides, at forest edges, and along roadsides. Also
native to Russia and Korea. Type specimen from Siberia, Russia.

30a. **Narrow-Leaf Single-Flower Iris**
var. *caricina* Kitagawa in Bot. Mag. Tokyo 49:232, f. 4. 1935.
Stem short, about 10 cm high; leaves 2 to 6 mm wide.
    Flowering in May, fruiting in June to August. Native to
Heilongjiang, Jilin, Liaoning, and Inner Mongolia. Grows in relatively dry grasslands or hillsides.

Section 3. Single-Bract Iris Section—Sect. *Ophioiris* Y. T. Zhao, Acta Phytotaxonomica Sinica 18(1):56. 1980.

31. **Single-Bract Iris** Snake Repellent, Spring Disappear (Hubei), Snake Disappear (Zhejiang), Enemies Never Meet (Guangxi), Summer Dormant (Jiangxi) Plate K:1–5
Iris anguifuga Y. T. Zhao, ex X. J. Xue, Acta Phytotaxonomica Sinica 18(1):56. 1980.
Perennial herb, green in winter, dry and wilted in summer, base surrounded by a few old leaves which persist as fibers. Rhizome thick, rounded and fat, creeping, maroon-red or yellowish brown always globular at the apex. Leaves linear, 20 to 30 cm long, 5 to 7 mm wide, apex acuminate or short acuminate, base sheathlike, with three to six parallel veins. Flower stem 30 to 50 cm high, with four or five leaflets, leaflets narrowly lanceolate, 8 to 12 cm long, about 5 mm wide; bract one, grassy, narrowly lanceolate, 10 to 13.5 cm long, about 8 mm wide, apex acuminate, like the leaflets on the upper stem, one flower in bract; flowers violet, about 10 cm in diameter; pedicel about 2.5 cm long; perianth tube slender, about 3 cm long, upper part slightly swollen, falls oblanceolate, 5 to 5.5 cm long, about 8 mm wide, marked with brown lines or dots, apex retuse, hafts narrow, standards narrowly oblanceolate, 4.5 to 5 cm long, about 3 mm wide, marked with bluish brown lines; stamens about 2.5 cm long, anthers bright yellow, filaments flat; style arms flat, 4.5 to 5 cm long, about 6 mm wide, crests slender, narrowly deltoid. Capsule three ridged, spindle shaped, 5.5 to 7 cm long, 1.5 to 2 cm in diameter, epicarp with yellowish brown pubescent trichomes, apex with long points, fruiting pedicel about 5 cm long; seed orbicular-globular, 4 to 5 mm in diameter. Flowering in late March to early April, for about one week, fruiting in May to July.

Native to Anhui, Hubei, and Guangxi. Grows on hillsides and in grassland. Cultivated in Zhejiang, Jiangxi, and Guizhou provinces. Type specimen from a cultivated plant at the Wuhan Botanical Garden, Academia Sinica, originally collected in Xianning, Hubei Province.

The rhizome is used for treatment of snake bite with apparent efficacy; can also be used as a laxative.

PLATE K 1–5. **Single-Bract Iris** *Iris anguifuga* Y. T. Zhao ex X. J. Xue: 1. Plant. 2. Rhizome. 3. Style arm. 4. Stamen. 5. Fruiting branch.
6–7. **Salt-Loving Iris** *Iris halophila* Pall.: 6. Plant. 7. Fruiting branch.
DRAWN BY YU ZHEN-ZHOU AND ZHAO YU-TANG)

Subgenus 2. Piano-Valve Iris Subgenus—Subgen. *Xyridion* (Tausch) Spach in Ann. Sci. Nat. ser. 3, 5:94. 1846; em. Rodion. The Genus Iris—*Iris* L. 191. 1961.—Iris Sect. *Xyridion* Tausch in Schultes, Additam. Mantis. 2:370. 1824, p.p.

Section 1. Piano-Valve Iris Section—Sect. *Xyridion* Tausch in Hort. Canalius, 1:1823.

32. **Salt-Loving Iris** (Key to Plants of Ulumuchi), Thick-Leaf Chinese Iris (Xinjiang) Plate K:6–7

Iris halophila Pall. Reise Russ. Reich. 3:713, t. B. f. 2. 1776;—*I. spuria* L. var. *halophila* (Pall.) Dykes, Gen. Iris 62. 1913;—*I. guldenstaedtiana* Lepech. in Act. Hort. Petrop. 5 (1):292, t. 8. 1781; Makino et Nemoto, Fl. Jap. ed. 2, 1591. 1931;—*I. desertorum* Ker-Gawl. in Curtis's Bot. Mag. t. 1514. 1812.

Perennial herb. Rhizome purple-brown, thick and large, 1.5 to 3 cm in diameter, creeping, with ringlike patterns, surface with persistent old leaf sheaths; roots thick and large, yellowish maroon, with wrinkled transverse patterns. Leaves sword shaped, grayish green, 20 to 60 cm long, 1 to 2 cm wide, slightly curved, with more than 10 parallel veins, without obvious midribs. Flower stem thick and large, 20 to 40 cm high, about 0.5 cm in diameter, shorter than the leaves, upper part with one to four lateral branches, lower part with one or two leaflets; bracts three, grassy, green, 5.5 to 9 cm long, about 2 cm wide, margin membranous, white, containing two flowers; flowers yellow, 5 to 6 cm in diameter; pedicel 1.5 to 3 cm long; perianth tube about 1 cm long, falls pandurate, about 4 cm long, about 1 cm wide, standards oblanceolate, about 3.5 cm long, 6 to 8 mm wide; stamens about 3 cm long, anthers yellow; style arms flat, about 3.5 cm long, about 6 mm wide, ovary narrowly spindle shaped, 3.5 to 4 cm long, upper part thin and long. Capsule elliptical-cylindrical, 6 to 9 cm long, 2 to 2.5 cm in diameter, greenish brown or purple-brown, with six raised, nearly paired ridges, apex with long points; at ripening, splitting at main ribs; seeds almost pomoid, 5 to 6 mm in diameter, yellow-maroon, pericarp membranous, thin paperlike, wrinkled, glossy. Flowering in May to June, fruiting in July to August.

Native to Gansu and Xinjiang. Grows in grasslands, hillsides, wastelands, pebbly slopes, and wet salty soils. Also native to Russia. Type specimen from Central Asia, USSR.

32a. **Blue-Flowered Salt-Loving Iris**

var. *sogdiana* (Bunge) Grubov in Information Syst. Imp. Pl. 1969:30. 1970;—*I. sogdiana* Bunge in Mem. Acad. Sci. St.

Petersb. Sav. Etrang. 7:507. 1851; B. Fedtsch. in Kom. Fl. URSS 4:526. 1935.

This variety has the same vegetative characteristics as *Iris halophila*, but has violet flowers, or has violet in the blades of falls and standards; hafts are yellow.

Habitat and distribution same as *Iris halophila*. Type specimen from USSR.

Subgenus 3. Nepal Iris Subgenus—Subgen. *Nepalensis* (Dykes) Lawr. in Gent. Herb. 8. fasc. 4:363. 1953.—*Iris* Sect. *Nepalensis* Dykes, Gen. Iris, 16; 184. 1913.

33. **Plateau Iris** (Yunnan List of Seed Plants), Small Palm Bundle (Iconographia Cormophytorum Sinicorum) Plate L:1–2
Iris collettii Hook. f. in Curtis's Bot. Mag. 129: t. 7889. 1903; Dykes, Gen. Iris 186. 1913; Liu Yin, Chinese Magazine of Botany 3(2):936. 1936; Iconographia Cormophytorum Sinicorum 5:572, Fig. 7974. 1976;—*I. duclouxii* Lévl. in Fedde, Repert. Sp. Nov. 6:113. 1908.

Perennial herb, stem base surrounded by maroon-brown hairy old leaves which persist as fibers. Rhizome short, nodes not obvious; roots swollen, slightly spindle shaped, maroon-brown, fleshy. Leaves basal, grayish green, linear or sword shaped; at flowering, leaves 10 to 20 cm long, 2 to 5 mm wide; at fruiting, leaves 20 to 35 cm long, 1.2 to 1.4 cm wide, apex acuminate, base sheathlike, with two to five parallel veins. Flower stem very short, not emerging from the ground, base surrounded by several membranous sheathlike leaves; bracts green, widely lanceolate or narrowly ovate, 2 to 4 cm long, apex acuminate, midribs obvious, containing one or two flowers; flowers dark blue or violet, 3 to 3.5 cm in diameter; perianth tube thin and long, upper part swollen to trumpet shaped, 5 to 7 cm long, 1 to 1.5 mm in diameter, falls elliptical-obovate, about 4.5 cm long, hafts narrow and long with orange beard on midrib, standards oblanceolate, about 3 to 3.5 cm long, erect; stamens about 2.3 cm long, anther yellow, filaments white; style arm petaloid, about 2 cm long, crests thin and long. Capsule green, three ridged, ovate, 1.5 to 2 cm long, 1.3 to 1.5 cm in diameter, apex with short point; at ripening it opens from the top down to one-third the length, bracts persistent on the fruit base; seeds long-elliptical, black-brown, not glossy, without aril. Flowering in May to June, fruiting in July to August.

Native to Sichuan, Yunnan, and Tibet. Grows on plateaus at an

altitude of 1650 to 3500 m in sunny, dry grasslands on hillsides. Also native to India, Burma, Nepal, and Thailand. Type specimen from Burma.

34. **Nepal Iris** (Chinese Magazine of Botany), Small Orchid Flower (Yunnan) Plate L:3–4

Iris decora Wall. Pl. As. Rar.1:77, t. 86. 1830; Lawr. in Gent. Herb. 8(4):363. 1953; Hara, Fl. E. Himal. Second report 175–176. 1971;—*I. nepalensis* D. Don, Prod. Fl. Nep. 54. 1825, non Wallich 1824; Hook. f. Fl. Brit. Ind. 6:273. 1892; Dykes, Gen. Iris 184, f. 25, pl. 39. 1913; Liu Yin, Chinese Magazine of Botany 3(2):935. 1936;—*I. yunnanensis* Lévl. in Fedde, Repert. Sp. Nov. 6:113. 1908;—*Junopsis decora* (Wall.) W. Schulze in Oesterr. Bot. Zeitschr. 117:327. 1969.

Perennial herb, stem base surrounded by many maroon-brown sheathlike old leaves which persist as fibers. Rhizome short and thick, tuberlike; roots swollen, spindle shaped, maroon-brown, fleshy, with wrinkled transverse patterns. Leaves linear; at flowering 10 to 20 (28) cm long, 2 to 3 (8) mm wide; at fruiting, up to 60 cm long, 6 to 8 mm wide, apex long acuminate, with two or three parallel veins. Flower stem 10 to 25 cm high, 2 to 3 mm in diameter; at fruiting, up to 35 cm high, upper part branched, one or two lanceolate leaflets on the middle, lower part; bracts three, membranous, green, lanceolate, 4.5 to 7 cm long, 1 cm wide, apex acuminate or long acuminate, containing two flowers; flowers violet or pale blue, 2.5 to 6 cm in diameter; pedicel 1 to 1.5 cm long; perianth tube slender and long, 2.5 to 3 cm long, upper part trumpetlike, falls long-elliptical or obovate, about 4 cm long, 1.8 cm wide, with yellow beard on midrib, standards narrowly elliptical or oblanceolate, about 4 cm long, about 1.2 cm wide; stamens about 2.5 cm long, anthers light yellowish white; style arms flat and wide, about 3.5 cm long, crests obtuse-deltoid, margin with few teeth. Capsule ovate-orbicular, 2.5 to 3.5 cm long, about 1 cm in diameter, apex with short points. Flowering in June, fruiting in July to August.

Native to Sichuan, Yunnan, and Tibet. Grows at an altitude of 1500 to 3000 m on wasteland and grassy hillsides of plateaus. Also native to India, Bhutan, and Nepal. Type specimen from Nepal.

PLATE L   1–2. **Plateau Iris** *Iris colletti* Hook f.: 1. Plant. 2. Fruiting branch. 3–4. **Nepal Iris** *Iris decora* Wall.: 3. Plant. 4. Fruiting branch.
DRAWN BY YU ZHEN-ZHOU

Subgenus 4. Vesper Iris Subgenus—Subgen. *Pardanthopsis* (Hance) Baker in Handb. Irideae 1. 1892. p. p.; Rodion. The Genus Iris—*Iris* L. 193. 1961.—*Iris* Sect. *Pardanthopsis* Hance in Journ. Bot. 13:105. 1875.

35. **Vesper Iris** (Flora of the Beijing Region), White Blackberry Lily (Outline of the Flora of Economic Plants of North China, Iconographia Cormophytorum Sinicorum), Dichotomous Iris (Chinese Magazine of Botany), Fan Grass (Hebei), Sheep Horn Grass (Jiangsu), Stork's Fan (Shanxi), Flat Cattail Fan (Shaanxi) Plate M:1

Iris dichotoma Pall. Reise Russ. Reich. 3:712. 1776; Maxim. in Bull. Acad. Sci. St. Petersb. 26:540. 1880; C. H. Wright in Journ. Linn. Soc. Bot. 36:81. 1903; Dykes, Gen. Iris 96. 1913; Kom. Fl. Mansh. 2:420. 1927; B. Fedtsch. in Kom. Fl. URSS 4:530. 1935; Liu Yin, Chinese Magazine of Botany 3(2):938. 1936; Kitagawa, Lineam. Fl. Mansh. 147. 1939; Key to Northeast Plants 587. 1959; Flora of the Beijing Area (Monocots) 301. 1975, excl. t. 329; Iconographia Cormophytorum Sinicorum 5:578 Fig. 7985. 1976; Flora of Qin Ling 1(1):938. 1976;—*Pardanthus dichotomus* Ledeb. Fl. Ross. 4:106. 1853.

Perennial herb. Rhizome irregularly tuberous, maroon, brown or dark brown; roots well developed, thick and long, yellowish white with few branches. Leaves basal or alternate at the base of the flower stem, both sides grayish green, sword shaped, 15 to 35 cm long, 1.5 to 3 cm. wide, apex slightly curved, acuminate, or shortly acuminate without obvious midrib. Flower stem solid 40 to 60 cm high, upper part dichotomous, branching region with lanceolate leaflets, lower part with one or two leaflets which surround the flower stem, inflorescence at apex of branches; bracts four or five, membranous, green, margin white, lanceolate, 1.5 to 2.3 cm long, containing three or four flowers; flowers violet or pale blue with maroon-brown markings, 4 to 4.5 cm in diameter; pedicel slender always emerging beyond bracts, 2 to 3.5 cm long; perianth tube very short, falls widely oblanceolate 3 to 3.5 cm long about 1 cm wide, blade pendant, without beard, standards narrowly obovate about 2.5 cm long, 6 to 8 mm wide, apex retuse; stamens 1.6 to 1.8 cm long; anthers and filaments equal in length; style arms flat, petaloid about 2.5 cm long, crests narrowly deltoid, ovary green

PLATE M   1. **Vesper Iris** *Iris dichotoma* Pall.: Plant.
2–4. **Zhongdian Iris** *Iris subdichotoma* Y. T. Zhao: 2. Plant. 3. Flowering branch. 4. Fruiting branch.
DRAWN BY YU ZHEN-ZHOU, ZHAO YU-TANG, AND LI XI-CHOU

about 1 cm long. Capsule cylindrical or slightly curved 3.5 to 5 cm long, 1 to 1.2 cm in diameter, pericarp yellowish green, coriaceous, when ripe splitting from apex about one-third down the length; seeds dark brown, elliptical with small wings.

Native to Heilongjiang, Jilin, Liaoning, Inner Mongolia, Hebei, Shanxi, Shandong, Henan, Anhui, Jiangsu, Jiangxi, Shaanxi, Gansu, Ningxia, and Qinghai. Grows in sandy grasslands and sunny dry areas between rocks on hillsides. Also distributed in USSR and Mongolia. Type specimen collected from eastern Siberia, USSR.

This species is similar in appearance to *Belamcanda chinensis;* however, *Iris dichotoma* has rhizomes which are relatively short, flowers violet or pale blue, style arms petaloid, fruits long and cylindrical, seeds with small wings.

36. **Zhongdian Iris** Plate M:2–4
Iris subdichotoma Y. T. Zhao, Acta Phytotaxonomica Sinica 18(1):57. 1980.
Perennial herb, stem base surrounded by maroon-brown old leaves which persist as fibers. Rhizome short; roots thick, with few branches. Leaves grayish green, sword shaped or wide-linear; at flowering, 20 to 25 cm long, 1 to 1.5 cm wide; at fruiting, up to 40 cm long, about 2 cm wide, apex acuminate, erect or slightly curved inward, base sheathlike, overlapping, without obvious midrib. Flower stem 25 to 40 cm high, with two to five branches on upper part; bracts three to five, green, margin membranous, 2.5 to 3.5 cm long, 7 to 8 mm wide, containing two to four flowers; flowers violet, about 5 cm in diameter; pedicel 3 to 4 cm long; perianth tube about 2 cm long, falls oblanceolate, about 4 cm long, about 7 mm wide, without beard on the midrib, standards narrowly lanceolate, about 3 cm long, about 4 mm wide; stamens about 2.2 cm long, filaments longer than anthers; style arms about 3 cm long, crests narrowly deltoid, ovary narrowly spindle shaped, about 1.5 cm long, about 0.5 cm in diameter. Capsule long cylindrical, 5 to 6 cm long, about 1 cm in diameter, with six slightly projecting ribs; when ripe splitting from top down one-third of the length; seeds maroon-brown, 7.5 to 8.5 mm long, with small wings. Flowering in June, fruiting in July to September.

Native to northwestern Yunnan. Grows at an altitude of 1800 to 2000 m in grasslands and along riversides, open hillsides, and banks near water. Type specimen from the Yangtze River side of Haba Shan, Snow Mountain, northwestern Yunnan.

This species is similar to *Iris dichotoma;* however this species has leaves erect or slightly curved, apex acuminate; inflorescence branches small; bracts 2.5 to 3.5 cm long; perianth tube about 2 cm long; flower purple or violet.

Subgenus 5. Cockscomb Crested Subgenus—Subgen. *Crossiris* Spach in Ann. Sci. Nat. ser. 3, 5:110. 1846.

Section 1. Cockscomb Crested Section—Sect. *Crossiris* in Ann. Sci. Nat. ser. 3, 5:110. 1846.

37. **Small Flowered Iris** (Flora of Guangzhou), Bright Purple Iris (Chinese Magazine of Botany), Eight-Ridged Hemp (Sichuan), Six-Wheeled Thatch (Guizhou) Plate N:1–4

Iris speculatrix Hance in Journ. Bot. 13:196. 1875, et in 14:75. 1876; Baker in Gard. Chron. ser. 2, 6:36. 1876, et in Curtis's Bot. Mag. t. 6306. 1877; Maxim. in Bull. Acad. Sci. St. Petersb. 26:538. 1880; Liu Yin, Chinese Magazine of Botany 3(2):938. 1936;—*I. grijsi* Maxim. in Bull. Acad. Sci. St. Petersb. 26:527. 1880; C. H. Wright in Journ. Linn. Soc. Bot. 36:82. 1903; Iconographia Cormophytorum Sinicorum 5:574, Fig. 7978. 1976;—*I. cavalariei* Lévl. Liliac. et C. Chine 18. 1905.

Perennial herb, stem base surrounded by maroon-brown old leaves which persist as fibers or lanceolate sheathlike leaves. Rhizome bifid, creeping, maroon-brown; roots relatively thick and large, with few branches. Leaves slightly curved, dark green, glabrous, sword shaped or linear, about 15 to 30 cm long, 0.6 to 1.2 cm wide, apex acuminate, base sheathlike, with three to five parallel veins. Flower stem glabrous and smooth, 20 to 25 cm high, with one or two leaflets; bracts two or three, grassy, green, narrowly lanceolate, 5.5 to 7.5 cm long, apex long-acuminate, containing one or two flowers; pedicel 3 to 5.5 cm long, after flowers fall, bent at a right angle; flower violet or light blue, 5.6 to 6 cm in diameter; perianth tube short and thick, about 5 mm long, falls spoon shaped, about 3.5 cm long, about 9 mm wide, with dark purple ringlike mottled marks, bright yellow crest on midrib, crest like a raised felt strip, standards narrow oblanceolate, about 3.7 cm long, about 9 mm wide, erect; stamens about 1.2 cm long, anthers white, longer than filaments; style arms flat, about 2.5 cm long, about 7 mm wide, same color as petals, crests long and slender, narrowly deltoid, ovary spindle shaped, green, 1.6 to 2 cm long, about 5 mm in diameter. Capsule elliptical, 5 to 5.5 cm long, about 2 cm in diameter, apex with long, slender, and sharp point, pedicels bent at right

angles after flowers fall; seed polyhedral, maroon-brown, with small wings on sides. Flowering in May, fruiting in July to August.

Native to Anhui, Zhejiang, Fujian, Hubei, Hunan, Jiangxi, Guangdong, Guangxi, Sichuan, and Guizhou. Grows on mountains, along roadsides, at forest edges, or in open groves. Type specimen from Hong Kong.

This species has a yellowish crest on the midrib of the falls, but this is difficult to see after the specimen has been pressed and dried. According to the literature, China has another species, *I. grijsi* Maxim., which has very similar characteristics to *I. speculatrix*. However *I. grijsi* has the same characters and distribution as *I. speculatrix* except that *I. grijsi* has no crest on the midrib of the falls. I believe it is possible that when Maximowicz inspected the specimens, he overlooked the fact that it is very difficult to see the crestlike ridge on the midrib of the falls after pressing, and he thus named it as a new species. Therefore, I believe that *I. grijsi* should be a synonym of *I. speculatrix*. Also according to Dykes' report, *I. grijsi* has branched flower stems, but this is also an individual phenomenon and insufficient to be the main characteristic of *I. grijsi*.

38. Taiwan Iris

Iris formosana Ohwi in Acta Phytotax. Geobot. 3:114–115. 1934; Nemoto, Fl. Jap. Suppl. 1086. 1936; T. S. Liu et S. S. Ying, Fl. Taiwan 5:141–143, pl. 1300. 1978.

Perennial herb. Rhizome thick and large, erect, with fingers or irregular branches. Leaves with bright green upper surface, grayish green below, sword shaped, 30 to 40 cm long, 2 to 2.5 cm wide, apex acuminate, base sheathlike, with three to five relatively obvious parallel veins. Flower stem erect, 30 to 40 cm high, with four to five branches; flower stem leaflets as long as the inflorescence branches; bracts four to six, green, margin membranous, midrib obvious, containing three to five flowers; flowers white, with light blue linear markings and yellow mottled patterns, 7 to 8 cm in diameter; pedicel flat deltoid, about 3 cm long; perianth tube white, about 1 cm long, falls obovate, 4 to 5 cm long, about 2.5 cm wide, blades pendant, white with sky blue to blue, linear pattern and yellow mottled pattern on white falls, base with yellow

PLATE N   1–4. **Small-Flowered Iris** *Iris speculatrix:* Hance: 1. Plant. 2. Fall. 3. Fruiting branch. 4. Seed.
5–6. **Wide-Styled Iris** *Iris latistyla* Y. T. Zhao: 5. Lower part of stem with rhizome and roots. 6. Flowering branch.
DRAWN BY YU ZHEN-ZHOU AND ZHAO YU-TANG

mottling, midrib with projecting crest, standards very pale blue, oblanceolate to oblong, 2.5 to 3 cm long, about 1.5 cm wide, outer half angled outward, surface with dense glandular trichomes, apex deeply incised; filaments white, about 1.5 cm long, anthers oblong to linear, 8 to 9 mm long; style arms cuneate, pale blue, about 2 cm long, 6 to 7 mm wide, crests about 1.5 mm long, ovary almost as long as the perianth tube, about 1 cm long. Capsule oblong to ovate-cylindrical, 3 to 4 cm long, apex with persistent perianth tube; seeds many.

Native to Taiwan. Grows on hillsides, at forest edges, or along roadsides at an altitude of 500 to 1000 m. Type specimen from northeastern Taiwan.

According to the literature, this species is similar to *Iris japonica*. Distinguishable points: *Iris formosana* has white powder on lower surface of leaves; bracts relatively wider and larger; flowers larger, petals with a shallowly incised margin, outer rim of falls pendant at flowering, perianth tube as long as ovary. (Based on edited and translated information.)

39. **Butterfly Flower** (Mirror of Flowers), Japanese Iris (Chinese Magazine of Botany), Open-Throat Arrow, Blue-Flower Grass, Flat Bamboo, Scissors Grass (Hunan), Soybean Grass, Slender-Pole Leaf, Flat-Bamboo Root (Sichuan), Iron-Bean Firewood (Guizhou) Plate O:1–3

Iris japonica Thunb. in Trans. Linn. Soc. 2:327. 1794; Baker in Gard. Chron. ser. 2, 6:37. 1876; Maxim. in Bull. Acad. Sci. St. Petersb. 26:538. 1880; C. H. Wright in Journ. Linn. Soc. Bot. 36:82. 1903; Dykes, Gen. Iris 99. 1913; Liu Yin, Chinese Magazine of Botany 3(2):936. 1936; Ohwi, Fl. Jap. 322. 1956; Makino, New Ill. Fl. Jap. 869. 1963; Iconographia Cormophytorum Sinicorum 5:573, Fig. 7976. 1976; Flora of Qin Ling 1(1):385. 1976; Flora of Jiangsu, First Volume 393. 1977;—*I. chinensis* Curt. in Curtis's Bot. Mag. t. 373. 1797;—*I. fimbriata* Vent. Jard. Cels. t. 9. 1800.

Perennial herb. Rhizome usually divided into two types: strongly erect and slenderly transverse; erect rhizome flat-orbicular, with many relatively short segments, maroon-brown; transverse rhizome with long segments, yellowish white; roots emerging from rhizome nodes, with many branches. Leaves basal, dark green, glossy, reddish purple near the ground, sword shaped, 25 to 60 cm long, 1.5 to 3 cm wide, apex acuminate, without obvious midribs. Flower stem erect, with five to twelve branches; three to five bracts, leaf shaped, wide lanceolate or ovate-orbicular, 0.8 to

1.5 cm long, apex obtuse, with two to four flowers; flowers pale blue or violet, 4.5 to 5.5 cm in diameter; pedicel longer than bract, 1.5 to 2.5 cm long; perianth tube obvious, 1.1 to 1.5 cm long, falls obovate or elliptical, 2.5 to 3 cm long, 1.4 to 2 cm wide, apex retuse, base cuneate, margin undulate, with fine teeth, midrib with projecting yellow crest, standards elliptical or narrowly obovate, 2.8 to 3 cm long, 1.5 to 2.1 cm wide, apex retuse, margin with fine teeth, angled outward at flowering; stamens 0.8 to 1.2 cm long, anthers long-elliptical, white; style arms slightly shorter than standards, midrib pale blue, crests fimbriate, ovary spindle shaped, 0.7 to 1 cm long. Capsule elliptical-cylindrical, 2.5 to 3 cm long, 1.2 to 1.5 cm in diameter, apex apiculate, base obtuse, six obvious parallel veins, opening from top down one-half of length at ripening; seed dark brown, irregularly polyhedral, without aril. Flowering in March to April, fruiting in May to June.

Native to Jiangsu, Anhui, Zhejiang, Fujian, Hubei, Hunan, Guangdong, Guangxi, Shaanxi, Gansu, Sichuan, Guizhou, and Yunnan. Grows in relatively wet grasslands on hillsides, grassland at edge of open forests, as well as on plateaus at an altitude of 3000 to 3300 m. Also native to Japan. Type specimen from Japan.

Used medicinally for reduction of fever and treatment of poisoning, cure of fever in children, pulmonary tuberculosis, sore throat, swelling, and other purposes.

39a. **White Butterfly Flower**
f. *pallescens* P. L. Chiu et Y. T. Zhao, Acta Phytotaxonomica Sinica 18(1):58. 1980.

Leaves and bracts both yellowish green; flowers white, about 5.5 cm in diameter; falls with pale yellow mottling or pale yellowish brown lines of mottling on midrib; style arms with faint pale blue color on midrib.

Native to Zhejiang. Habitat same as that of *Iris japonica*. Type specimen from Hangzhou Botanical Garden.

40. **Flat-Bamboo Orchid** Flat-Bamboo Root, Flat Bamboo (Yunnan, Sichuan) Plate O:4–10
Iris confusa Sealy in Gard. Chron. ser. 3, 102:414. in adnot. 432. 1937;—*I. wattii* auct. non. Baker: Dykes in Gard. Chron. ser. 3, 57:95. 1915. p. p. maj.

Perennial herb. Transverse rhizome, 4 to 7 mm in diameter, yellowish brown, nodes obvious, segments relatively long; roots with many branches, yellowish brown or light yellow. Stem erect, 80 to 120 cm high, flat cylindrical, segments obvious, with persistent old leaf-sheaths at the nodes. Leaves about 10 per fan, base sheathlike, leaves sword shaped, 28 to 80 cm long, 3 to 6 cm wide, yellowish green, both surfaces somewhat glaucous, apex acuminate, without obvious vertical veins. Flower stem 20 to 30 cm long, branches of inflorescence clustered with four to six membranous bracts; bracts ovate, about 1.5 cm long, obtuse, with 3 to 5 flowers; flowers pale blue or white, 5 to 5.5 cm in diameter; pedicel as long or slightly longer than bract; perianth tube about 1.5 cm long, falls elliptical, about 3 cm long, about 2 cm wide, apex retuse, margin undulate, slightly toothed, standards widely oblanceolate, about 2.5 cm long, about 1 cm wide, apex retuse; stamens about 1.5 cm long, anthers yellowish white; style arms pale blue, about 2 cm long, about 8 mm wide, crests fimbriate; ovary green, cylindrical spindle shaped, about 6 mm long. Capsule elliptical, 2.5 to 3.5 cm long, 1 to 1.4 cm in diameter, with a pattern of netted veins or six obvious veins on the upper surface; seed dark brown, 3 to 4 mm long, about 2.5 mm wide, without aril. Flowering in April, fruiting in May to July.

Native to Guangxi, Sichuan, and Yunnan. Grows at forest edges, under open groves, near wet ditches, or in grasslands on hillsides. Type specimen from Techang, Sichuan.

Rhizome can be used medicinally for cure of acute tonsillitis and acute bronchitis.

This species has flowers and fruits similar to *Iris japonica* and vegetative parts similar to *Iris wattii*. These characters must be closely observed or they can be confused.

41. **Fan-Shaped Iris** (Handbook of Cultivated Plants of the Lushan Botanical Garden) Flat-Bamboo Orchid, Iron Fan, Old God's Fan (Yunnan) Plate O:11–15

Iris wattii Baker, Handb. Irid. 17. 1892; Hook. f. Fl. Brit. Ind. 6:273. 1892; Liu Yin, Chinese Magazine of Botany 3(2):937. 1936; Sealy in Curtis's Bot. Mag. t. 9590. 1940;—*I. milesii* auct. non Foster: Dykes, Gen. Iris. 101. 1913.

Perennial herb. Rhizome thick, large, about 1 cm in diameter, running transversely, with obvious segments, long, yellowish white;

PLATE O   1–3. **Butterfly Flower** *Iris japonica* Thunb.: 1. Plant. 2. Flowering branch. 3. Fruiting branch.
4–10. **Flat-Bamboo Orchid** *Iris confusa* Sealy: 4. Base of stem. 5. Upper part of stem with flowering stalk. 6. Flowering branch. 7. Stamen. 8. Style arm (lower surface). 9. Style arm (upper surface). 10. Fruiting branch.
11–15. **Fan-Shaped Iris** *Iris wattii* Baker: 11. Leaf section. 12. Flowering branch. 13. Fall 14. Standard. 15. Split capsule.
DRAWN BY ZENG XIAO-LIAN, YU ZHEN-ZHOU, AND JIANG ZU-DE

root branches relatively many, yellowish white. Erect stem cylindrical, 50 to 100 cm high, 1 to 1.5 cm in diameter, nodes obvious, with persistent old leaf sheaths. Leaves yellowish green, surface lightly pleated, about 10 leaves on each stem apex, bases overlapping with each other, leaves wide sword shaped, 50 to 70 cm long, 5 to 7 cm wide, apex acuminate, base sheathlike, with more than 10 parallel veins. Flower stem 30 to 50 cm high, about 7 mm in diameter; panicle racemose with five to seven branches; three to five bracts on each branch, membranous, green, lanceolate to narrow ovate, 1.5 to 2.5 cm long, about 1 cm wide, apex obtuse, containing two to four flowers; flowers violet, 7.5 to 8 cm in diameter; pedicel about 1.5 cm long; perianth tube trumpet shaped, about 2 cm long, falls obovate, 4.5 to 5 cm long, 2.4 to 2.8 cm wide, with deep purple mottling or linear patterns, margin undulate, ruffled, midrib with irregular yellowish crest, standards oblanceolate or narrowly obovate, 3.5 to 4 cm long, 1 to 1.3 cm wide, inclined outward at flowering; stamens about 3 cm long, anthers yellow, filaments white; style arms pale blue, smooth, curved, 3 to 3.5 cm long, 0.8 to 1 cm wide, crests fimbriate, ovary green, spindle shaped, 7 to 8 mm long. Capsule elliptical, 2.8 to 3.5 cm long, 1.3 to 1.5 cm in diameter, apex mucronate, without obvious point, with six veins, three veins obvious and raised; seed maroon-brown, flat, semiorbicular, about 4 mm in diameter. Flowering in April, fruiting in May to August.

Native to Yunnan and Tibet. Grows in grasslands at forest edge or wet riversides at an altitude of about 2000 m. Also native from India to Bhutan. Type specimen from northeastern India.

This species is always confused with the Flat-Bamboo Orchid, *Iris confusa*. The difference between them is that this species has flowers that are larger, 7.5 to 8 cm in diameter, while *Iris confusa* has relatively small flowers, 5 to 5.5 cm in diameter. In addition, Hook. f. in *Flora of British India* claimed that this species has no beard or crest on the falls as originally reported by Baker, although this claim is possibly derived from careless observation.

42. **Wide-Styled Iris** Plate N:5–6

Iris latistyla Y. T. Zhao, Acta Phytotaxonomica Sinica 18(1):61. 1980.

Perennial herb, stem base surrounded by maroon-brown or gray-brown old leaves which persist as fibers. Rhizome very short, not obvious; roots fleshy, fat, pale maroon, with wrinkled transverse patterns. Leaves basal, grayish green, narrowly linear, 15 to 25 cm long, 2 to 3 mm wide, with two or three parallel veins, apex long acuminate, base sheathlike. Flower stem 6 to 14 cm high, about 2 mm in diameter, not branched or with one lateral branch. Bracts three, membranous, green, narrowly lanceolate, 2.5 to 4.5 cm long, 6 to 8 mm wide, apex acuminate, containing two flowers; flower violet, about 5 cm in diameter; falls obovate, 3.5 to 4 cm long, about 1.5 cm wide, blades pendant, hafts cuneiform, midrib with crest, standards widely lanceolate, or narrowly ovate, about 3.5 cm long, about 1.5 cm wide; style arms flat and broad, about 4 cm long, about 1.5 cm wide, crests wide and large, deltoid, margin slightly toothed. Flowering in May to June, fruiting in July to September.

Native to Tibet. Grows at forest edges, grasslands near paddy sides, at an altitude of 3100 to 4000 m. Type specimen from Nyingchi County, Tibet.

43. **Roof Iris** (Shen Nung's Classics of Medicinal Plants), Roof Iris (Chinese Magazine of Botany), Blue Butterfly (Guangdong), Purple Butterfly, Flat-Bamboo Flower (Shanxi), Frog Seven (Hubei) Plate P:1–3

Iris tectorum Maxim. in Bull. Acad. St. Petersb. 15:380. 1871; Hook. f. in Curtis's Bot. Mag. t. 6118. 1874; Baker in Gard. Chron. ser. 2, 6:37. 1876; Dykes, Gen. Iris 102, pl. 24(a). 1913; Liu Yin, Chinese Magazine of Botany 3(2):937. 1936; Ohwi, Fl. Jap. 333. 1956; Iconographia Cormophytorum Sinicorum 5:573, Fig. 7975. 1976; Flora of Qin Ling 1(1):386. 1976;—*I. rosthornii* Diels in Engl. Bot. Jahrb. 29:261. 1910;—*I. chinensis* Bunge, Enum. Pl. Chin. Bor. Coll. 64. 1833; non Curtis. 1797.

Perennial herb, stem base surrounded by old leaves which persist as membranous sheaths or fibers. Rhizome thick and large, branched, about 1 cm in diameter, creeping; roots relatively slender and short. Leaves basal, yellowish green, middle portion slightly wider, widely sword shaped, 15 to 50 cm long, 1.5 to 3.5 cm wide, apex acuminate or short acuminate, base sheathlike, with several not obvious, parallel veins. Flower stem glabrous, 20 to 40 cm high, apex always with one or two short lateral branches, middle and lower part with one or two leaflets; bracts two or three, green, grassy, margin membranous, pale, lanceolate or long ovate-orbicular, 5 to 7.5 cm long, 2 to 2.5 cm wide, apex acuminate or long acuminate, containing one or two flowers; flowers violet, about 10 cm in diameter; pedicel very short; perianth tube slender and long, about 3 cm long, upper end swollen, trumpet shaped, falls orbicular or widely ovate, 5 to 6 cm long about 4 cm wide, apex retuse, midrib with irregular crest, standards elliptical, 4.5 to 5 cm long,

about 3 cm wide, spreading horizontally at flowering; stamens about 2.5 cm long, anthers bright yellow, filaments long and slender, white; style arms flat, pale blue, about 3.5 cm long, crests nearly four sided with few teeth, ovary spindle shaped cylindrical, 1.8 to 2 cm long. Capsule long elliptical or obovate, 4.5 to 6 cm long, 2 to 2.5 cm in diameter, with six obvious veins, splitting into three valves at ripening; seeds black-brown, pomoid, without appendages. Flowering in April to May, fruiting in June to August.

Native to Shanxi, Anhui, Jiangsu, Zhejiang, Fujian, Hubei, Hunan, Jiangxi, Guangxi, Shaanxi, Gansu, Sichuan, Guizhou, Yunnan, and Tibet. Grows on sunny banks, at forest edges, and at wet watersides. Type specimen from Japan.

43a. White-Flowered Roof Iris

f. *alba* Makino, Ill. Fl. Nipp. 714. 1940;—var. *alba Dykes,* Gen. Iris 103. 1913.

Flowers white, falls with light yellow mottling on claw; other characteristics are the same as those of *Iris tectorum.*

Native to Zhejiang (Hangzhou Xiatianzhu). Cultivated in many gardens.

44. Red-Flowered Iris (Yunnan List of Seed Plants)

Iris milesii Baker ex M. Foster in Gard. Chron. new ser. 20:231. 1883; Baker in Curtis's Bot. Mag. t. 6889. 1886; Hook. f. Fl. Brit. Ind. 6:273. 1892; Dykes, Gen. Iris 101. 1913; Liu Yin, Chinese Magazine of Botany 3(2):937. 1936.

Perennial herb. Rhizome thick and stout, 1 to 1.5 cm in diameter, nodes obvious. Stem obviously erect, 60 to 90 cm high, base slightly thickened, nodes obvious, lower nodes with persistent yellowish brown old leaf sheaths. Leaves grayish green on both sides, widely sword shaped, 40 to 60 cm long, 2.5 to 5 cm wide, parallel veins obvious. Upper flower stem with two to four branches, each branch 15 to 20 cm long, base with lanceolate leaflets; bracts several, membranous, 2.5 to 3.5 cm long, 2 to 2.5 cm wide, containing three or four flowers; pedicel 2.5 to 4 cm long, semirounded in cross section; flowers pale reddish purple, with relatively dark lines and mottling, 7 to 8 cm in diameter; perianth

---

PLATE P   1–3. **Roof Iris** *Iris tectorum* Maxim.: 1. Lower part of stem with rhizome. 2. Upper part of stem with flower. 3. Fruiting branch.
4–7. **Small Iris** *Iris proantha* Diels: 4. Plant. 5. Fall. 6. Standard. 7. Style arms and stamen.
8–9. **Larger Small Iris** *Iris proantha* Diels var. *valida* (Chien) Y. T. Zhao: 8. Plant. 9. Fruiting branch.
DRAWN BY YU ZHEN-ZHOU

tube 1 to 1.5 cm long, falls obovate, with purple brown mottled pattern, margin incised, midrib with orange-yellow crest, standards narrowly obovate, 4 to 5 cm long, apex retuse, held horizontally at flowering, margin with few undulate teeth; stamens about 2.5 cm long, anthers milky white; style arms pale violet, about 3 cm long, crests square, margins fimbriate, ovary dark green, three ridged cylindrical, about 3 cm long. Capsule ovate-orbicular, pericarp coriaceous, with obvious netted veins; seeds pomoid, black, with small white aril. Flowering in April to May, fruiting in June to August.

Native to Sichuan, Yunnan, and Tibet. Grows at forest edges on hillside or open groves and wet places. Also native to India. Type specimen from Manipur, India.

Section 2. Small Iris Section—Sect. *Lophiris* Tausch in Hort. Canalius, 1. 1823; em. Rodion. The Genus Iris—*Iris* L. 194.1961.

45. **Small Iris** (Flora of Jiangsu) Russian Mimic Iris (Chinese Magazine of Botany) Plate P:4–7

Iris proantha Diels in Svensk. Bot. Tidskr. 18:427. 1924;—*I. pseudorossii* Chien, Syn. nov. in Contr. Biol. Lab. Sci. Soc. China Bot. ser. 6:72–74. 1931; Liu Yin, Chinese Magazine of Botany 3(2):952. 1936; Flora of Jiangsu (First Volume) 394. 1977;—*I. rossii* auct. non. Baker,: Steward, Man. Vasc. Pl. Low. Yangtze China 256. 1958.

Small perennial, stem base pale green, surrounded by three to five sheathlike leaves or a few old leaves which persist as fibers. Rhizome long and slender, dichotomous, creeping, maroon-yellow, nodes swollen; roots delicate and slender, emerging from nodes, maroon-yellow. Leaves narrowly linear, yellowish green, 5 to 20 cm long at flowering, 1 to 2.5 mm wide, up to 40 cm long at fruiting, up to 7 mm wide, apex long acuminate, base sheath shaped, with one or two parallel veins. Flower stem 5 to 7 cm high, lower half with one or two sheathlike leaflets; bracts two, grassy, green, narrowly lanceolate, 3.5 to 5.5 cm long, about 6 mm wide, apex acuminate, containing one flower; flowers pale violet, 3.5 to 4 cm in diameter; pedicel 0.6 to 1 cm long; perianth tube 2.5 to 3 (5) cm long, falls obovate, about 2.5 cm long, 1 to 1.2 cm wide, horizontal at flowering, with horseshoe-shaped mottled pattern, midrib with yellow crest, crest like a raised felt strip, standards oblanceolate, 2.2 to 2.5 cm long, about 7 mm wide, erect; stamens about 1 cm long, both filaments and anther white; style arms pale violet, about 1.8 cm long, about 4 mm wide, crests long deltoid, margin entire with few teeth, ovary green, cylindrical, 4 to 5 mm long. Capsule globular, 1.2 to 1.5 cm in diameter, apex with short points; fruiting pedicel 1 to 1.3 cm long, bract persistent on fruit base. Flowering in March to April, fruiting in May to July.

Native to Anhui, Jiangsu, Zhejiang, Hubei, and Hunan. Grows on hillsides, in grassland, at forest edges, or in open groves. Type specimen from Chu Xian County, Anhui.

According to Diel's original description of *Iris proantha:* without a beard on the fall, this species should be in the sect. *Apogon* (subgen. *Limniris* in Rodionenko's system); actually this species has a crest and should belong to sect. *Evansia* (subgen. *Crossiris* in Rodionenko's system). After the specimen has been pressed and dried, the crest is not easily seen, which is very likely the cause of descriptive errors. Later, Chien Chong-shu reported that he found a crest in this species, so he named it *Iris pseudorossii* Chien (1931). I think the two names are synonyms for the same species, and although Diel has some mistakes, his description is still valid. In addition, when we compare the years of publication, *Iris pseudorossii* should be treated as a synonym of *Iris proantha*.

45a. **Larger Small Iris** Large-flowered variety of Russian Mimic Iris (Chinese Magazine of Botany) Plate P:8–9

var. *valida* (Chien) Y. T. Zhao, com. nov;—*I. pseudorossii* Chien var. *valida* Chien in Contr. Biol. Lab. Sci. Soc. China Bot. ser. 6:74–75. 1931; Liu Yin, Chinese Magazine of Botany 3(2):952. 1936.

All parts of this variety are larger than in *Iris proantha;* stem 20 to 28 cm high. Leaves about 27 cm long and about 7 mm wide at flowering, up to 55 cm long and about 8 mm wide at fruiting. Flower stem 20 to 28 cm high; flowers pale violet, about 5 cm in diameter; pedicel about 1 to 2 cm long; perianth tube 3 to 6 cm long, falls about 2.6 cm long, about 9 mm wide, standards 2 to 2.2 cm long, about 7 mm wide; stamens about 7 mm long; style arms about 1.6 cm long. Flowering in April, fruiting in May to July.

Native to Zhejiang. Grows in open fields, in forests, or along roadsides. Type specimen from West Tien Mu Mountain, Zhejiang.

Subgenus 6. Bearded Iris—Subgenus *Iris*—*Pogoniris* Spach in Ann. Sci. Nat. Ser. 3, 5:103. 1846.

Section1. Fruit Apex-Opening Section—Sect. *Iris*—*Pogoniris* Spach in Ann. Sci. Nat. Ser. 3, 5:103. 1846.

46. **German Iris** Plate Q:1–2

Iris germanica L. Sp. Pl. 38. 1753; Ker-Gawl. in Curtis's Bot. Mag. 18:t. 670. 1803; Baker in Journ. Linn. Soc. Bot. 16:146. 1877; Dykes, Gen. Iris 162. 1913; B. Fedtsch. in Kom. Fl. URSS 4:553. 1935; Bailey, Man. Cult. Pl. 271. 1949; Flora of the Beijing Region 300, Fig. 327. 1975; Iconographia Cormophytorum Sinicorum 5:574, Fig. 7977. 1976.

Perennial herb. Rhizome thick, stout and fat, branched, flattened cylindrical, creeping, yellowish brown; roots fleshy, yellowish white. Leaves erect or slightly curved, pale green, grayish green or dark green, always glaucous, sword shaped, 20 to 50 cm long, 2 to 4 cm wide, apex acuminate, base sheathlike, always reddish brown, without obvious midrib. Flower stem glabrous, yellowish green, 60 to 100 cm high, upper part with one to three lateral branches, middle, lower part with one to three leaflets; bracts three, grassy, green, margin membranous, sometimes with pale reddish purple color, ovate-orbicular or widely ovate, 2 to 5 cm long, 2 to 3 cm wide, containing one or two flowers; flowers large, brightly colored, up to 12 cm in diameter; flower color various according to cultivar, many pale purple, violet, dark purple, or white, fragrant; perianth tube trumpet shaped, about 2 cm long, falls elliptical or obovate, 6 to 7.5 cm long, 4 to 4.5 cm wide, blades pendulous, midrib with dense yellow beard, standards obovate or orbicular, about 5 cm long and wide, erect, apex curved inward, midrib wide; stamens 2.5 to 2.8 cm long, anthers milky white; style arms pale blue, violet or white, about 5 cm long, about 1.8 cm wide, crests wide-deltoid or semirounded, ovary spindle shaped, about 3 cm long, about 5 mm in diameter. Capsule three ridged cylindrical, 4 to 5 cm long, apex obtuse, without points, opening downward into three valves at ripening; seeds pomoid, yellowish maroon, surface

PLATE Q   1–2. **German Iris** *Iris germanica* L.: 1. Leaf fan with rhizome. 2. Upper part of flower stem.
3–4. **Manchurian Iris** *Iris mandshurica* Maxim.: 3. Plant. 4. Fruiting branch.
5–7. **Central Asian Iris** *Iris bloudowii* Ledeb.: 5. Plant. 6. Fruiting branch. 7. Seed.

DRAWN BY YU ZHEN-ZHOU

with wrinkled patterns, apex without an aril. Flowering in April to May, fruiting in June to August.

Native to Europe. Cultivated in many gardens in China. Famous for many cultivars and forms.

47. **Fragrant-Root Iris** (English-Latin-Chinese Plant Names)
Iris pallida Lamarck Encycl. 3:294. 1789; Ker-Gawl. in Curtis's Bot. Mag. 18:t. 685. 1803; Dykes Gen. Iris 166. 1913; Bailey, Man. Cult. Pl. 272. 1949.

Perennial herb. Rhizome thick, stout and long, flattened cylindrical, up to 2.5 cm in diameter, creeping, with ring patterns, yellowish brown or maroon; roots stout, yellowish white. Leaves grayish green, outer surface glaucous, sword shaped, 40 to 80 cm long, 3 to 5 cm wide, apex short acuminate, base sheathlike, without obvious midvein. Flower stem glabrous, green, glaucous, 50 to 100 cm high, 1.3 to 1.5 cm in diameter, upper part with one to three lateral branches, middle and lower part with one to three leaflets; bracts three, membranous, silver-white, ovate-orbicular or wide ovate-orbicular, 3 to 3.5 cm long, 2.5 to 3 cm wide, containing one or two flowers; flowers large, violet, pale blue, or purple-red, up to 12 cm in diameter; perianth tube trumpet shaped, about 2 cm long, falls elliptical or obovate, 6 to 7.5 cm long, 4 to 4.5 cm wide, apex pendulous, claw narrowly cuneate, midrib with dense yellow beard, standards orbicular or obovate, about 5 cm long and wide, erect, apex curved inward, claw narrowly cuneate; stamens 2.5 to 2.8 cm long, anthers milky white; style arms petaloid, about 5 cm long, about 1.8 cm wide, crests wide deltoid or semirounded, ovary spindle shaped, about 3 cm long, about 5 mm in diameter. Capsule ovate-orbicular-cylindrical, 4.5 to 4.7 cm long, 2.5 to 3.5 cm in diameter, apex obtuse, without points, splitting open into three valves at ripening; seeds pomoid, maroon-brown, without an aril. Flowering in May, fruiting in June to September.

Native to Europe, cultivated in many gardens in China.

The rhizome of this species is used in fine perfumes and cosmetics, and it has medicinal and chemical uses.

Similar to *Iris germanica*, but differs in its membranous, white bracts, whereas *Iris germanica* has bracts which are grassy green in the lower part and have a membranous, reddish purple margin.

Section 2. Fruit Side-Splitting Section—Sect. *Hexapogon* (Bunge) Baker in Gard. Chron. ser. 3, 5:787–788 1876; in Rodion. The Genus Iris—*Iris* L. 198. 1961;—*Iris* Subgen. *Hexapogon* Bunge ex Alef. in Bot. Ztg. 21:296. 1863. p. p.

48. **Curved-Leaf Iris** Plate R:1–2

Iris curvifolia Y. T. Zhao, Acta Phytotaxonomica Sinica 20 (1) 99. 1982.

Perennial herb. Rhizome large and thick, about 2 cm in diameter, creeping, yellowish maroon; roots thick, with few branches. Leaves with thickened base, surrounded by old leaves that persist as membranous sheaths, curved sickle shaped or with slightly curved upper half, 10 to 20 cm long, 1 to 1.5 cm wide, apex short acuminate or acuminate, middle part slightly wider, base sheathlike, swollen, overlapping. Flower stem 8 to 10 cm high, without leaflets; bracts three, lanceolate, 5 to 6 cm long, 1.3 to 1.8 cm wide, apex acuminate, containing two flowers; flowers bright yellow, with brown lines, 4.5 to 6 cm in diameter; perianth tube with thicker upper part and thinner lower part, 2 to 3 cm long, falls obovate, about 4.5 cm long, about 1.5 cm wide, claw long and slender, narrowly cuneate, midrib with pale yellow beard, standards oblanceolate, about 4 cm long, about 1.3 cm wide; stamens about 2.2 cm long, anthers yellow; style arms about 3 cm long, about 4 mm wide, crests angled, lanceolate, ovary cylindrical, 1.8 to 2.2 cm long. Capsule obovate, about 4 cm long, about 2 cm in diameter, apex rounded, with short point, pericarp yellowish green, glabrous, with six obvious veins; seed obliquely pomoid, about 7 mm long, reddish brown. Flowering in May to June, fruiting in July to September.

Native to Xinjiang. Grows in grasslands on hillsides. Type specimen from Xinjiang.

This species has a yellow flower with a beard on the midrib of falls which is similar to *Iris bloudowii*. The distinguishing points: this species has leaves curved and sickle shaped, leaf sheath swollen; bracts lanceolate, apex acuminate; fruit obovate, apex rounded, surface glabrous.

49. **Manchurian Iris** (Key to Northeast Plants) Northeast Iris (Key to the Flora of Northeastern China) Plate Q:3–4

Iris mandshurica Maxim. in Bull. Acad. St. Petersb. 26:530. 1880; Kom. Fl. Mansh. 2:418. 1927; Dykes, Gen. Iris 140. 1913; Liu Yin, Chinese Magazine of Botany 3(2):949. 1936; Kitagawa, Lineam. Fl. Mansh. 148. 1939; Key to Northeast Plants 586. 1959.

Perennial herb, stem base surrounded by maroon-brown old leaves which persist as fibers. Rhizome short and thick, large, fleshy, tuberlike; roots almost fleshy, with thick upper and thinner lower part, with few branches, yellowish white. Leaves curved sicklelike or with slightly curved upper half, about 10 to 15 cm long and 0.5 to 1 cm wide at flowering, up to 30 cm long and about 1.5 cm wide at fruiting, apex acuminate or shortly acuminate, base sheathlike, with two to four parallel veins, without obvious midrib. Flower stem glabrous, base with lanceolate sheathlike leaflet, 15 to 20 cm high; bracts three, membranous, green, obovate or lanceolate, 3.5 to 5 cm long, 1 to 1.8 cm wide, midrib obvious, apex short acuminate, containing one or two flowers; flowers yellow, 4 to 5 cm in diameter; pedicel 6 to 7 mm long; perianth tube narrowly funnel shaped, 2 to 2.5 cm long, falls obovate, 4 to 4.5 cm long, 1.5 to 2 cm wide, with maroon-veined patterns, claw narrowly cuneate, midrib with dense yellow beard, standards angled outward, narrowly elliptical or oblanceolate, about 3.5 cm long; stamens about 2 cm long, anthers yellow; style arms flat, about 3 cm long, 4 to 5 mm wide, crests relatively wide and large, semirounded, with few teeth, ovary green, spindle shaped, 1 to 1.2 cm long. Capsule spindle shaped, about 6 cm long, about 1.5 cm in diameter, with six obvious veins (three of six are slightly more obvious), apex acuminate with long point, splitting along ridges at ripening, points and base not splitting. Flowering in May, fruiting in June to August.

Native to Heilongjiang, Jilin, Liaoning. Grows on sunny banks and among shrubs near open groves. Also native to USSR. and Korea. Type specimen from southern part of northeast China.

50. **Central Asia Iris** (Handbook of Cultivated Plants of Lushan Botanical Gardens) Plate Q:5–7

Iris bloudowii Ledeb. Icon. Fl. Ross. 2:5, t. 101. 1830, et Fl. Alt. 4:331. 1833, et Fl. Ross. 4:102. 1853; Baker in Gard. Chron. ser. 2, 6:710. 1876; Maxim. in Bull. Acad. Sci. St. Petersb. 24:533. 1880; Dykes, Gen. Iris 138. 1913; B. Fedtsch. in Fl. URSS 4:550. 1935;—*I. flavissima* Pall. β *bloudowii* Baker, Handb. Irid. 29. 1892;—*I. flavissima* Pall. α *umbrosa* Bunge in Ledeb. Fl. Alt. 1:60. 1892.

Perennial herb, stem base surrounded by maroon-brown old

PLATE R 1–2. **Curved-Leaf Iris** *Iris curvifolia* Y. T. Zhao: 1. Plant. 2. Capsule.
3–4. **Membrane-Bract Iris** *Iris scariosa* Willd.: 3. Plant. 4. Capsule.
5–6. **Gansu Iris** *Iris pandurata* Maxim.: 5. Plant. 6. Capsule.
DRAWN BY YU ZHEN-ZHOU AND HE RUI-WU

leaves which persist as slender fibers and membranous sheathlike leaves. Rhizome thick and tough, enlarged, some parts swollen and segmented, maroon-brown; roots yellowish white. Leaves grayish green, sword shaped or linear, not curved or only slightly curved, 8 to 12 cm long and 4 to 8 mm wide at flowering, 15 to 25 cm long and 0.8 to 1.2 cm wide at fruiting, apex short acuminate, base sheath-like, overlapping, with five or six parallel veins, without obvious midribs. Flower stem 8 to 10 cm high, up to 30 cm long at fruiting, not branched; bracts three, membranous, with somewhat reddish purple color, obovate, about 4 cm long, 1.6 to 2 cm wide, apex obtuse, middle bract slightly shorter and narrower, containing two flowers; pedicel 0.6 to 1 cm long; flowers bright yellow, 5 to 5.5 cm in diameter; perianth tube funnel shaped, about 1 to 1.5 cm long, falls obovate, about 4 cm long, about 2 cm wide, blades curved, claw narrowly cuneate, midrib with beard, standards oblanceolate, 3 to 4.5 cm long, 1 to 1.2 cm wide, erect; stamens 1.8 to 2.2 cm long; style arms flat, bright yellow, crests deltoid, about 2.5 cm long, ovary green, spindle shaped, about 1.5 cm long, 3 to 5 mm in diameter. Capsule ovate-orbicular, six obvious veins, with irregular net pattern between veins, apex without obvious point, splitting along ridges at ripening; fruiting pedicel 1 to 1.2 cm long; seed elliptical, about 5 mm long, about 3 mm wide, deep brown, with white aril on one side. Flowering in May, fruiting in June to August.

Native to Heilongjiang, Jilin, and Xinjiang. Grows on sunny dunes and grasslands at forest edges. Also native to USSR. Type specimen from Altai Mountains.

51. **Gold-Bearded Iris** (Key to Northeast Plants) Yellow-Flowered Iris (Chinese Magazine of Botany) Yellow Iris (Key to the Flora of Northeastern China)
Iris flavissima Pall. Reise Russ. Reich. 1:715. 1771; Ledeb. Fl. Alt. 4:332. 1883; Baker in Gard. Chron. ser. 2, 6:710. 1876; Maxim. in Bull. Acad. Sci. St. Petersb. 26:530. 1880; Dykes, Gen. Iris 137. 1913; B. Fedtsch. in Kom. Fl. URSS 4:545. 1935; Liu Yin, Chinese Magazine of Botany 3(2):948. 1936; Kitagawa, Lineam. Fl. Mansh. 147. 1939;—*I. humilis* Georgi, Bemerk. Reise Russ. Reich. 1:196. 1775;—*I. arenaria* Waldst. et. Kit. Pl. Rar. Hung. 1:57, t. 57. 1802;—*I. dahurica* Herb. ex. Klatt in Bot. Zeit. 30:514. 1872.
Perennial herb, stem base with pale maroon old leaves which persist as fibers. Rhizome very short, woody, brown; roots thick and long, few branched, yellowish white. Leaves linear, 5 to 15 cm long, 1.5 to 3 mm wide at flowering, up to 30 cm long and about 5 mm

wide at fruiting, apex acuminate, without obvious midrib. Flower stem very short, not emerging or only slightly emerging from the ground, base with membranous yellowish white sheathlike leaflets; bracts membranous, two or three, narrowly lanceolate, apex acuminate, with one or two flowers; flowers yellow, 4 to 5 cm in diameter; perianth tube trumpet shaped, 2.5 to 3.5 cm long, falls elliptical or obovate, 3 to 3.5 cm long, 0.6 to 1.2 cm wide, with maroon-brown linear patterns, claw cuneate, midrib with beard, standards oblanceolate, 2.5 to 3 cm long, about 4 mm wide, erect; stamens about 2 cm long, anthers yellow; style arms bright yellow, about 2.5 cm long, crests narrowly long-deltoid, ovary cylindrical. Capsule spindle shaped, 3.5 to 4.5 cm long, 1 to 1.5 cm in diameter, apex without points, always with persistent perianth tube, base with persistent bracts. Flowering in April to May, fruiting in June to August.

Native to Heilongjiang, Inner Mongolia, Ningxia, and Xinjiang. Grows on dry grasslands, hillsides, and dunes. Also native to USSR and Mongolia. Type specimen from Trans-Baikal, USSR.

52. **Membrane-Bract Iris** Sickle-Leaf Chinese Iris (Xinjiang Traditional Chinese Herbal Medicine) Plate R:3–4

Iris scariosa Willd. ex Link. in Engl. Bot. Jahrb. 1 (3):71. 1820; Ledeb. Fl. Ross. 4:104. 1853; Maxim. in Bull. Acad. Sci. St. Petersb. 26:534. 1880; B. Fedtsch. in Kom. Fl. URSS 4:550. 1935.

Perennial herb, stem base surrounded by few old leaves which persist as slender fibers. Rhizome thick, tough, swollen, 1.5 to 2.2 cm in diameter, creeping, maroon-yellow; roots yellowish white, upper and lower parts of equal thickness, few branches. Leaves grayish green, sword shaped or curved sicklelike, 10 to 18 cm long, 1 to 1.8 cm wide, apex short acuminate, base yellow-white sheathlike, middle part relatively wide. Flower stem about 10 cm long, without leaflets; bracts three, membranous, margin reddish purple, long-ovate to wide-lanceolate, 4 to 5.5 cm long, 1.5 to 2 cm wide, apex short acuminate, containing two flowers; flowers violet, 5.5 to 6 cm in diameter; pedicel very short, perianth tube about 1.5 cm long, upper part enlarged trumpet shaped, falls obovate, about 6 cm long, about 1.5 cm wide, claw narrowly cuneate, midrib with yellow beard, standards oblanceolate, about 5 cm long, about 5 mm wide, erect; stamens about 1.8 cm long; style arms pale purple, about 3.5 cm long, crests narrowly deltoid, ovary spindle shaped, about 1.5 cm long. Capsule spindle shaped or ovate-orbicular-cylindrical, 5 to 7.5 cm long, 2.5 to 3 cm in diameter, apex without obvious point, but slightly swollen and ring shaped, six projecting veins, splitting along ridges at ripening. Flowering in April to May, fruiting in June to July.

Native to Xinjiang. Grows on sunny stony hillsides or beside ditches. Also native to USSR. Type specimen from Siberia, USSR.

53. Gansu Iris Plate R:5–6

Iris pandurata Maxim. in Bull. Acad. Sci. St. Petersb. 26:529. 1880;—*I. tigridia* auct. non Bunge: Dykes, Gen. Iris 153. 1913. p.p.

Perennial herb, stem base surrounded by many hairlike yellowish brown old leaves which persist as slender fibers. Rhizome tuberlike, very short; roots thick and strong, almost fleshy, upper and lower halves of equal thickness, with fine, slender lateral roots, yellowish brown. Leaves grayish green, linear, 10 to 25 cm long, 1.5 to 4 mm wide, apex long acuminate, with three to five parallel veins, without obvious midrib. Flower stem solid, 3 to 12 cm high, base with several scalelike, membranous, lanceolate leaves; bracts two or three, membranous, lanceolate, 3.5 to 6 cm long, 1 to 1.5 cm wide, apex acuminate, with two flowers; flowers reddish purple, about 5 cm in diameter; without pedicel (sessile) or with very short pedicel; perianth tube slender, 2 to 3 cm long, upper part slightly thicker, falls about 4.5 cm long, about 1.4 cm wide, narrowly obovate, blade curved outward, claw narrowly cuneate, midrib with yellow beard, standards erect, oblanceolate, 3.5 cm long, about 8 mm wide; stamens about 2.5 cm long, anthers purple, the same length as filaments, ovary spindle shaped, about 1.5 cm long, 2 to 8 mm in diameter. Capsule ovate-orbicular, about 3.5 cm long, about 1.5 cm in diameter, six obvious veins, apex sharp, with short point, splitting along ridges at ripening; seed pomoid, about 4 mm long, about 2 mm in diameter, reddish brown, surface wrinkled, without aril. Flowering in May, fruiting in June to August.

Native to Gansu and Qinghai. Grows on hillsides, in grasslands, or along banks of ditches. Type specimen from the Yellow River Valley, western Gansu.

Dykes stated that *Iris pandurata* should be combined with *Iris tigridia* (Thick-Root Iris). However, *Iris pandurata* has longer roots which are equally thick in the upper and lower portions and which have many small lateral roots. Flowers are mainly two, rarely one; native to northwest China. *Iris tigridia* has relatively thick root bases, gradually tapering to root apex with wrinkled transverse patterns and extremely small lateral roots, and it is native to northeast China and Inner Mongolia.

54. **Sichuan Iris** Plate S:1–2
Iris sichuanensis Y. T. Zhao, Acta Phytotaxonomica Sinica 18(1):59. 1980.

Perennial herb, stem base with few hairy yellowish brown old leaves which persist as slender fibers and membranous sheathlike leaves. Rhizome irregularly tuberous, thick and stout, enlarged, 1.2 to 1.5 cm in diameter, dark brown or yellowish brown; roots thin and short, brown. Leaves grayish green, linear, 25 to 35 cm long, 0.5 to 1 cm wide, apex long-acuminate, midrib obvious. Flower stem 13 to 20 cm high, with one or two sheathlike leaflets; bracts three or four, membranous, green, wide-lanceolate to narrow-ovate, 4 to 8 cm long, 1.5 to 1.8 cm wide, apex short-acuminate, midrib obvious, containing two or three flowers; flowers violet, about 6 cm in diameter; pedicel very short; perianth tube 4 to 5 cm long, lower part filiform, upper part swollen, funnel shaped, falls obovate, 5 to 5.5 cm long, about 2 cm wide, claw narrow-cuneate, midrib with yellowish beard, standards erect, narrowly lanceolate, about 4 cm long, about 1 cm wide; stamens about 4 cm long; style arms flat, about 4.5 cm long, crests irregular-deltoid, ovary narrowly spindle shaped, 2.5 to 3 cm long. Fruit ovate-cylindrical, about 4 cm long, about 1.3 cm in diameter, apex with short point. Flowering in April, fruiting in May to July.

Native to Gansu and Sichuan. Grows among grass along roadsides and on hillsides. Type specimen from Wenchuan, Sichuan.

55. **Thin-Leaf Iris** Mao Ju Wormwood (Sichuan) Plate S:3
Iris leptophylla Lingelsheim in Fedd. Repert. Sp. Nov. Beih. 12:325. 1922.

Perennial herb, stem base with few yellowish maroon-brown hairy old leaves which persist as fibers or lanceolate membranous sheathlike leaves. Rhizome thick, fleshy, globular or irregularly tuberlike, yellowish brown or grayish brown; roots hairy soft, yellowish white, with few branches. Leaves thin, linear, 20 to 30 cm long, 2 to 3 mm wide, apex long-acuminate, midrib one. Flower stem slender, 15 to 35 cm high, about 2 mm in diameter, middle and lower parts with one leaflet, lanceolate, 8 to 9 cm long, apex acuminate; bracts three, membranous, green, margin semitransparent, lanceolate, 3.5 to 4.5 cm long, about 1 cm wide, apex short-acuminate, midrib obvious, containing two flowers; flowers violet, 3.5 to 4 cm in diameter; pedicel very short or flower sessile; perianth tube trumpetlike, about 3.5 cm long, up to 1.5 cm in diameter, falls obovate or spoon shaped, about 5 cm long, about 2 cm wide, claw narrow-cuneate, midrib with beard, standards narrow-oblanceolate, about 3.5 cm long, about 5 mm wide; stamens about 1 cm long, anthers white; style arms pale blue, with blue-white linear patterns. Capsule ovate-orbicular, 2 to 2.5 cm long, 1.5 to 2 cm in diameter, six obvious veins, dry perianth persistent at apex, capsule opening down one-third along ridges at ripening; seeds pomoid, dark brown, with maroon aril. Flowering in April to May, fruiting in May to June.

Native to Gansu and Sichuan. Grows in forests, and at forest edges on shaded hillsides. Type specimen from Wenchuan, Sichuan.

Rhizome can be used to treat diarrhea.

56. Narcissus Iris Plate S:4–7

Iris narcissiflora Diels in Svensk Bot. Tidskr. 18:428. 1924.

Perennial herb, stem base surrounded by sheathlike leaves, without basal leaves. Rhizome erect or running, erect rhizome short thick, maroon-brown, running rhizome slender and long; roots thin, yellowish white; leaves soft, linear, 2 to 3 mm wide, as long as or slightly shorter than flower stem, apex obtuse, base sheathlike, surrounding stem, without obvious midrib. Flower stem slender, not branched, 20 to 30 cm high; bracts two, membranous, lanceolate, 2.8 to 3.3 cm long, about 1.2 cm wide, apex acuminate, arching outward, containing one flower; flowers yellow, 5 to 5.5 cm in diameter; no pedicel (sessile); perianth tube 6 to 7 mm long, falls elliptical or obovate, about 3.5 cm long, about 2 to 2.2 cm wide, claw cuneate, midrib with sparse beard, standards narrow-ovate, about 3 cm long, about 1.8 cm wide, horizontal at flowering; stamens about 1.3 cm long, anthers shorter than filaments; style arms flat, middle part slightly wider, about 1.5 cm long, about 8 mm wide, crests irregular, elliptical, margin with undulate teeth, ovary spindlelike, about 1.5 cm long. Flowering in April to May, fruiting in June to August.

Native to Sichuan. Grows in grasslands on hillsides, in open spots in forests, and along forest edges or among shrubs. Type specimen from western Sichuan.

PLATES 1–2. **Sichuan Iris** *Iris sichuanensis* Y. T. Zhao: 1. Plant. 2. Fruiting branch.
3. **Thin-Leaf Iris** *Iris leptophylla* Lingelsheim: Plant.
4–7. **Narcissus Iris** *Iris narcissiflora* Diels: 4. Flower. 5. Flower (side view). 6. Fall. 7. Style arms and stamen.
DRAWN BY YU ZHEN-ZHOU

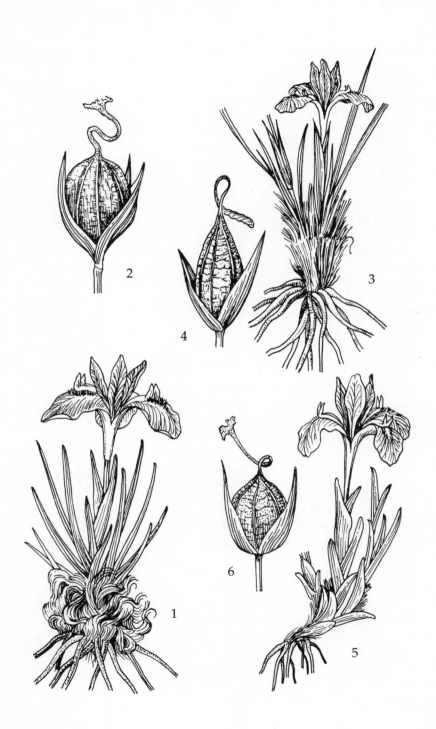

57. **Curled-Sheath Iris** (Iconographia Cormophytorum Sinicorum) Plate T:1–2

Iris potaninii Maxim. in Bull. Acad. Sci. St. Petersb. 26:528. 1880; Iconographia Cormophytorum Sinicorum 5:576, Fig. 7981. 1976;—*I. thoroldi* Baker ex Hemsl. in Journ. Linn. Soc. Bot. 30:118. 129. 1894, et in Hook. Icon. Pl. 24, t. 2302. 1894.

Perennial herb, stem base surrounded by many old leaves which persist as sheathlike fibers, maroon-brown or yellowish brown, hairlike, curly. Rhizome woody, tuberlike, very short; roots thick and long, yellowish white, almost fleshy, with few branches. Leaves linear, 4 to 8 cm long and 2 to 3 mm wide at flowering, up to 20 cm long and 3 to 4 mm wide at fruiting. Flower stem short, not emerging above ground, with one or two sheathlike leaflets; bracts two, membranous, narrowly lanceolate, 4 to 4.5 cm long, about 6 mm wide, apex acuminate, containing one flower; flowers yellow, about 5 cm in diameter; pedicel very short or absent; perianth tube 1.5 to 3.7 cm long, lower part slender, upper part trumpet shaped, falls obovate, about 3.5 cm long, about 1.2 cm wide, apex retuse, midrib with dense yellow beard, standards oblanceolate, about 2.5 cm long, 0.8 to 1 cm wide, apex retuse, erect; stamens about 1.5 cm long, anthers short and wide, purple; style arms flat, yellow, about 2.8 cm long, about 6 mm wide, crests semirounded, margin with irregular teeth, ovary spindle shaped, about 7 mm long. Capsule elliptical, 2.5 to 3 cm long, 1.3 to 1.6 cm wide, apex with short point, splitting along ridges at ripening, apices remaining connected with each other; seed pomoid, about 3 mm in diameter, maroon, surface wrinkled. Flowering in May to June, fruiting in July to September.

Native to Gansu, Qinghai, and Tibet. Grows on stony or dry hillsides above 3000 m in altitude. Also native to USSR, Mongolia, and India.

57a. **Blue-Flowered Curled-Sheath Iris**

var. *ionantha* Y. T. Zhao, Acta Phytotaxonomica Sinica 18(1):59. 1980.

Flowers violet, other characteristics, habitat, and distribution are the same as those of *Iris potaninii*.

Maximowicz reported that *Iris potaninii* has sulphur-yellow flowers. Later Dykes reported that it has yellow or violet flowers.

PLATE T 1–2. **Curled-Sheath Iris** *Iris potaninii* Maxim.: 1. Plant 2. Capsule.
3–4. **Thick-Root Iris** *Iris tigridia* Bunge: 3. Plant. 4. Capsule.
5–6. **Kumon Iris** *Iris kemaonensis* D. Don ex Royle: 5. Plant. 6. Capsule.
DRAWN BY YU ZHEN-ZHOU AND ZHAO YU-TANG

Considering the originally described characteristics, I think the latter, with violet flowers, should be a new variety.

58. **Thick-Root Iris** (Key to Northeast Plants) Mimic Tiger Iris (Chinese Magazine of Botany) Thick-Root Chinese Iris (Northeastern China) Plate T:3–4

Iris tigridia Bunge in Ledeb. Fl. Alt. 1:60. 1829; Ledeb. Icon. Pl. Ross. t. 342. 1833; Maxim. in Bull. Acad. Sci. St. Petersb. 26:530. 1880; C. H. Wright in Journ. Linn. Soc. Bot. 36:85. 1903; Dykes, Gen. Iris 153. 1913; B. Fedtsch. in Kom. Fl. URSS 4:549. 1935; Liu Yin, Chinese Magazine of Botany 3(2):947. 1936; Kitagawa, Lineam. Fl. Mansh. 149. 1939; Iconographia Cormophytorum Sinicorum 5:575. 1976. p.p.

Perennial herb, stem base always with many old leaves which persist as sheathlike fibers, not curled, maroon-brown. Rhizome not obvious, short and small, woody; roots fleshy, 3 to 4 mm in diameter, with wrinkled transverse patterns, yellowish white or yellowish brown, gradually tapering to apex, base slightly thicker, not branched or with few branches; leaves deep green, glossy, narrowly linear, 5 to 13 cm long and 1.5 to 2 mm wide at flowering, up to 30 cm long and about 3 mm wide at fruiting, apex long-acuminate, base sheathlike, membranous, relatively pale, without obvious midrib. Flower stem slender, 2 to 4 cm long, not emerging or barely emerging from the ground; bracts two, yellowish green, membranous, narrowly lanceolate, apex short-acuminate, containing one flower; flowers violet, 3.5 to 3.8 cm in diameter; pedicel about 5 mm long; perianth tube about 2 cm long, upper part gradually thicker, falls narrow-obovate, about 3.5 cm long, about 1 cm wide, with purple-brown to white mottling, claw cuneate, midrib with yellow beard, standards oblanceolate, 2.5 to 2.8 cm long, 4 to 5 mm wide, apex retuse, flaring outward at flowering; stamens about 1.5 cm long; style arms flat, about 2.3 cm long, crests narrow-deltoid, ovary green, narrowly spindle shaped, about 1.2 cm long. Capsule ovate-orbicular or elliptical, 3.5 to 4 cm long, 1.5 to 2 cm in diameter, pericarp coriaceous, apex acuminate, dry perianth persistent at apex, splitting down to base at ripening; seeds maroon-brown, pomoid, with yellowish white aril. Flowering in May, fruiting in June to August.

Native to Heilongjiang, Jilin, Liaoning, Inner Mongolia, and Shanxi. Grows on dunes, in sandy grasslands, or on dry hillsides. Also native to USSR and Mongolia.

58a. Large Thick-Root Iris

var. *fortis* Y. T. Zhao, Acta Phytotaxonomica Sinica 18(1):60. 1980. Characteristics to distinguish this variety from *Iris tigridia:* leaves relatively longer and wider, 10 to 20 cm long, 3 to 6 mm wide; flower stem 10 to 20 cm high, 1.5 to 2 mm in diameter; bracts 4 to 5 cm long, 8 to 10 mm wide; flowers violet, 4.5 to 5 cm in diameter; perianth tube about 2.5 cm long, falls obovate, about 5 cm long, about 1.5 cm wide, standards oblanceolate, about 4 cm long, about 8 mm wide; stamens about 2 cm long; style arms about 2.5 cm long, crests irregular-deltoid, ovary about 1.8 cm long. Flowering in May, fruiting in June to August.

Native to Jilin, Inner Mongolia, and Shanxi. Grows in grassland on sunny hillsides and forest edges. Type specimen from Lungtan Mountain, Jilin City.

59. Angular-Fruited Iris (Chinese Magazine of Botany) Small Raft Grass (Sichuan) Plate U:1–2

Iris goniocarpa Baker in Gard. Chron. ser. 3, 6:710. 1876; Hook. f. Fl. Brit. Ind. 6:274. 1892; Dykes, Gen. Iris 133. 1913; Liu Yin, Chinese Magazine of Botany 3(2):947. 1936; Iconographia Cormophytorum Sinicorum 5:576, Fig. 7982. 1976; Flora of Qin Ling1(1):386, Fig. 376. 1976;—*I. gracilis* Maxim. in Bull. Acad. Sci. St. Petersb. 26:527. 1880.

Perennial herb. Rhizome short, maroon-brown; roots thin, soft, yellowish white, somewhat branched. Leaves soft, yellowish green, linear, 10 to 25 cm long, 2 to 3 mm wide, apex obtuse, midrib not obvious. Flower stem 10 to 25 cm high, without leaflets; bracts two, membranous, green, tinted pale red, lanceolate, 2 to 4 cm long, 5 to 8 mm wide, apex acuminate, curved outward, containing one flower; flowers violet, 3.5 to 5 cm in diameter; pedicel very short or absent; perianth tube 1.5 to 2 cm long, falls obovate or elliptical, 2.5 to 3 cm long, about 1 cm wide, with deep purple mottling, apex retuse, base cuneate, midrib with beard, base of hairs white, tips yellow, standards narrowly elliptical or oblanceolate, 1.8 to 2.2 cm long, about 5 mm long, apex retuse, erect; stamens about 1.5 cm long, anthers yellow; style arms petaloid, about 1.8 cm long, crests narrow-deltoid, ovary green, 1 to 1.5 cm long. Capsule yellowish maroon, three ridged cylindrical, 3.2 to 4 cm long, 1.2 to 1.8 cm in diameter, apex with short point. Flowering in May to June, fruiting in June to August.

Native to Shaanxi, Gansu, Qinghai, Sichuan, Yunnan, and Tibet. Grows in high mountain grasslands at 3000 to 4000 m altitude, on sunny hillsides, at forest edges, and in open groves. Also native to India, Sikkim, Bhutan, and Nepal. Type specimen from Sikkim.

59a. Large Angular-Fruited Iris
var. *grossa* Y. T. Zhao, Acta Phytotaxonomica Sinica 18(1):60. 1980. Distinguishing points of this variety: larger and thicker, about 30 cm high; leaves 25 to 28 cm long, about 5 mm wide; flowers larger, 7 to 8 cm in diameter.

Native to Sichuan, Yunnan, and Tibet. Grows in grasslands on hillsides, at forest edges, or in open woods. Type specimen from Sichuan.

59b. Slender Angular-Fruited Iris Plate U:3
var. *tenella* Y. T. Zhao, Acta Phytotaxonomica Sinica 18(1):60. 1980.
More delicate than *Iris goniocarpa:* 20 to 23 cm high; leaves 15 to 22 cm long, about 2 mm wide; flowers 2.5 to 3 cm in diameter; perianth tube long and slender, longer than bracts, 1 to 1.2 cm long.

Native to Qinghai. Grows on sunny banks. Type specimen from Xunhua, Qinghai.

60. Kumon Iris (Chinese Magazine of Botany) Plate T:5–6
Iris kemaonensis D. Don ex Royle, Ill. Bot. Himal. 1:372. 1839; D. Don in Trans. Linn. Soc. Lond. 18:311 1840; Hook. f. Fl. Brit. Ind. 6:274. 1892, "Kumaonensis;" Dykes, Gen. Iris 130, pl. 30. 1913; Liu Yin, Chinese Magazine of Botany 3(2):946. 1936; Hara, Fl. E. Himal. Second Report 176. 1971; H. Hara, W. T. Stearn and L. H. J. Williams, Enum. Fl. Pl. Nepal 1:64. 1978;—*I. kamaonensis* Wall. Numer. List. 177. n. 5052, 1831–1832, nom. nud.;—*I. kingiana* Foster Gard. Chron. 1:611. 1887; Baker in Curtis's Bot. Mag. 113:t. 6957. 1887.

Perennial herb, stem base surrounded by membranous sheathlike leaves or grayish maroon old leaves which persist as fibers. Rhizome short and thick, enlarged; roots long and thin, upper and lower portions equally thick, yellowish white. Leaves soft, yellowish green, linear, 6 to 10 cm long and about 2 to 4 mm wide at flowering, up to 9 to 15 cm long and 3 to 7 mm wide at fruiting, apex obtuse, without obvious midribs. Flower stem very short, not emerging from the ground, 2 to 3 cm long, base with membranous,

PLATE U   1–2. **Angular-Fruited Iris** *Iris goniocarpa* Baker: 1. Plant. 2. Capsule.
3. **Slender Angular-Fruited Iris** *Iris goniocarpa* Baker var. *tenella* Y. T. Zhao: Plant.
DRAWN BY ZHAO YU-TANG AND YU ZHEN-ZHOU

lanceolate sheathlike leaves; bracts two or three, membranous, green, wide lanceolate 5 to 6 cm long, 1 to 1.8 cm wide, apex acuminate, containing one flower; flowers dark purple or violet, 5 to 6 cm in diameter; pedicel 1 to 1.5 cm long, perianth tube trumpet shaped, 5.5 to 6 cm long, upper part gradually thicker, thickest part up to 7 to 8 mm in diameter; falls long obovate, about 4.5 cm long, 2.3 to 2.5 cm wide with deep purple dappling or linear patterns, claw cuneate, midrib with beard, base of hairs white, tips yellow; standards obovate, about 4 cm long about 1.5 cm wide, erect; stamens blue, 2 to 2.3 cm long, style arms flat, angled, deep purple about 3.2 cm long, about 6 mm wide, slightly curved, crests deltoid, crenate, ovary spindlelike about 6 mm long. Capsule globular or ovate-orbicular 2 to 2.5 cm long, 1.5 to 1.8 cm in diameter, six obvious veins, apex with a short point, seed reddish brown, polyhedral with a milky yellow aril.

Native to Sichuan, Yunnan, and Tibet. Grows among grasses on hillsides, and in valleys at an altitude of 3500 to 4200 m. Also native to India, Burma, Bhutan, and Nepal. Type specimen from India.

APPENDICES

Appendix 1

CHINESE AND ENGLISH NAMES OF CHINESE IRIS

The problem of common names has been difficult and trouble-some. There are few widely recognized common names for most iris species anywhere. In an attempt to reduce the confusion inherent in translations, we have listed below a transliteration of the Chinese characters for the primary common name used in the original Chinese text. The Chinese common name is followed by its English translation, and then, where applicable, further discussion. A few are direct translations of Latin names.

1. (Huanghua Yuan Wei) Yellow-Flowered Iris *I. wilsonii* C. H. Wright
2. (Yunnan Yuan Wei) Yunnan Iris *I. forrestii* Dykes
3. (Beiling Yuan Wei) North Tombs Iris *I. typhifolia* Kitagawa
   Beiling is located in Shenyang City (Mukden), Liaoning Province. The words literally refer to the North Tombs of the Qing Dynasty (1616–1912).
4. (Yuchanhua) Jade Cicada Flower *I. ensata* Thunb.
   In the West this is usually refered to as the Japanese Iris.
5. (Jinmai Yuan Wei) Gold-Vein Iris *I. chrysographes* Dykes
   Named for the prominent golden veins on the falls.
6. (Siberia Yuan Wei) Siberian Iris *I. sibirica* L.
   The Chinese common name is simply a series of characters that sound like the word Siberia.
7. (Xisun) Bloodred Iris *I. sanguinea* Donn ex Horn.
   Oddly there is no English common name for this widely grown species. It is usually referred to, along with *I. sibirica*, simply as Siberian Iris. The Latin name also refers to the blood-red color, but the flowers are usually in blue, violet, or purple shades. A white form is also known.
8. (Xinan Yuan Wei) Southwest Iris *I. bulleyana* Dykes
9. (Changting Yuan Wei) Long-Scape Iris *I. delavayi* Mich.
10. (Xizang Yuan Wei) Tibet Iris *I. clarkei* Baker

11. (Yanzihua) Swallow Flower *I. laevigata* Fisch.
12. (Wusuli Yuan Wei) Ussuri Iris *I. maackii* Maxim.
    The Wusuli (Ussuri) River forms a portion of the border between Heilongjiang Province and the USSR. In China the pinyin name is Wusuli, but the Russian name is Ussuri. It flows north to the Amur River and then northeast to the Sea of Okhotsk.
13. (Huang Changpu) Yellow-Flag Iris *I. pseudacorus* L.
14. (Bianse Yuan Wei) Varied-Color Iris *I. versicolor* L.
15. (Xiao Huanghua Yuan Wei) Small Yellow-Flowered Iris *I. minutoaurea* Makino
16. (Changwei Yuan Wei) Long-Tailed Iris *I. rossii* Baker
17. (Changbing Yuan Wei) Long-Pedicel Iris *I. henryi* Baker
18. (Shan Yuan Wei) Mountain Iris *I. setosa* Pall. ex Link
19. (Baihua Malin) White-Flowered Chinese Iris *I. lactea* Pall.
    This is a widely grown species without any common name. This name is a good start for this underappreciated species.
20. (Xiye Yuan Wei) Slender-Leaf Iris *I. tenuifolia* Pall.
21. (Ai Yuan Wei) Tiny Iris *I. kobayashii* Kitagawa
22. (Qinghai Yuan Wei) Qinghai Iris *I. qinghainica* Y. T. Zhao
23. (Huaxia Yuan Wei) Cathay Iris *I. cathayensis* Migo
    Huaxia is an alternate name for the entire country and of course the old name of Cathay needs no further explanation.
24. (Tian Shan Yuan Wei) Tian Shan Mountain Iris *I. loczyi* Kanitz
    Tian Shan means Sky Mountain and is a range of mountains (Shan) running from northern Xinjiang Province to the USSR.
25. (Doban Yuan Wei) Many-Spotted Iris *I. polysticta* Diels
26. (Zhungar Yuan Wei) Songar Iris *I. songarica* Schrenk
    Songar is a basin north of Tian Shan in Xinjiang Province.
27. (Ta Bao Yuan Wei) Large-Bract Iris *I. bungei* Maxim.
28. (Nanghua Yuan Wei) Pouch-Flowered Iris *I. ventricosa* Pall.
29. (Zibao Yuan Wei) Purple-Bract Iris *I. ruthenica* Ker-Gawl.
30. (Danhua Yuan Wei) Single-Flowered Iris *I. uniflora* Pall. ex Link
31. (Danbao Yuan Wei) Single-Bract Iris *I. anguifuga* Y. T. Zhao
32. (Xiyan Yuan Wei) Salt-Loving Iris *I. halophila* Pall.
33. (Gaoyuan Yuan Wei) Plateau Iris *I. collettii* Hook. f.
34. (Nepal Yuan Wei) Nepal Iris *I. decora* Wall.
35. (Ye Yuan Wei) Vesper Iris *I. dichotoma* Pall.
36. (Zhongdian Yuan Wei) Zhongdian Iris *I. subdichotoma* Y. T. Zhao
    Zhongdian is a location in northwest Yunnan Province.
37. (Xiaohua Yuan Wei) Small-Flowered Iris *I. speculatrix* Hance
38. (Taiwan Yuan Wei) Taiwan Iris *I. formosana* Ohwi

39. (Hudiehua) Butterfly Flower *I. japonica* Thunb.
40. (Bianzhulan) Flat-Bamboo Orchid *I. confusa* Sealy
41. (Shanxing Yuan Wei) Fan-Shaped Iris *I. wattii* Baker
42. (Kuanzhu Yuan Wei) Wide-Styled Iris *I. latistyla* Y. T. Zhao
43. (Yuan Wei) Roof Iris *I. tectorum* Maxim.
    The common name in the West is Japanese Roof Iris or simply Roof Iris.
44. (Honghua Yuan Wei) Red-Flowered Iris *I. milesii* Baker ex M. Foster
    Although this is the only common name of which we are aware for this species, the color is not red, but rather a pale red-violet.
45. (Xiao Yuan Wei) Small Iris *I. proantha* Diels
46. (Degue Yuan Wei) German Iris *I. germanica* L.
47. (Xianggen Yuan Wei) Fragrant-Root Iris *I. pallida* Lam.
48. (Wanye Yuan Wei) Curved-Leaf Iris *I. curvifolia* Y. T. Zhao
49. (Changbei Yuan Wei) Manchurian Iris *I. mandshurica* Maxim.
    Changbai refers to an isolated group of mountains in southeast Jilin Province; however, the distribution of this species is not confined to this small area.
50. (Zhongya Yuan Wei) Central Asian Iris *I. bloudowii* Ledeb.
51. (Huangjin Yuan Wei) Gold-Bearded Iris *I. flavissima* Pall.
52. (Mebao Yuan Wei) Membrane-Bract Iris *I. scariosa* Willd. ex Link
53. (Gansu Yuan Wei) Gansu Iris *I. pandurata* Maxim.
54. (Sichuan Yuan Wei) Sichuan Iris *I. sichuanensis* Y. T. Zhao
55. (Beye Yuan Wei) Thin-Leaf Iris *I. leptophylla* Lingelsheim
56. (Shuixienhua Yuan Wei) Narcissus Iris *I. narcissiflora* Diels
57. (Juanchiao Yuan Wei) Curled-Sheath Iris *I. potaninii* Maxim.
58. (Cugen Yuan Wei) Thick-Root Iris *I. tigridia* Bunge
59. (Ruiguo Yuan Wei) Angular-Fruited Iris *I. goniocarpa* Baker
60. (Kumen Yuan Wei) Kumon Iris *I. kemaonensis* D. Don ex Royle
    This species is usually spelled as "kamaonensis" and is based on the type location of the Kumon Mountain Range in northern Burma. This location has been variously spelled as "Kamaon," "Kumaon," and "Kemaon," but current atlas usage designates the site as Kumon. The species name has been the source of some confusion. This is Zhao's spelling, referring to the synonymy given in this species' account. See also the recent review of this nomenclature by Mathew, 1990.

Appendix 2

PROVINCES OF CHINA:
PINYIN AND TRADITIONAL NAMES

In the text the names of the provinces are given in their pinyin spelling. Various attempts have been made to provide a phonetic system for pronouncing Chinese characters. The old system, based on the 19th century Wade-Giles system, was officially replaced in modern China in 1958 by the pinyin (literally "phonetic transcription") pronunciations. This has been the cause for such apparent changes as Peking to Beijing and Szechuan to Sichuan. The actual names in China remain unchanged. Following are the currently used names for China's provinces, based on the official name for these provinces. The pinyin names are given in the far left column. Older maps may show the traditional (Wade-Giles) names given in the far right column. A few provinces are officially known under formal names which are given in the middle column. The exceptions are the provinces of Xizang Zizhiqu and Nei Menggu Zizhiqu, for which this text retains the traditional spelling and names of Tibet and Inner Mongolia.

APPENDIX 2. PROVINCES OF CHINA: PINYIN AND TRADITIONAL NAMES

Pinyin name	Official name	Traditional name
Anhui		Anwei
Fujian		Fukien
Gansu		Kansu
Guangdong		Kwangtung
Guangxi	Guangxi Zhuangzu Zizhiqu	Kwangsi Chuang Autonomous Region
Guizhou		Kweichow
Heilongjiang		Heilongkiang
Hebei		Hopei (Hopeh)
Henan		Honan
Hubei		Hupei (Hupeh)
Hunan		Hunan
Nei Menggu	Nei Menggu Zizhiqu	Inner Mongolia Autonomous Region
Jiangsu		Kiangsu
Jiangxi		Kiangsi
Jilin		Kirin
Liaoning		Liaoning
Ningxia	Ningxia Huizu Zizhiqu	Ninghsia Hui Autonomous Region
Qinghai		Tsinghai
Shandong		Shantung
Shaanxi		Shenhsi
Shanxi		Shanhsi
Sichuan		Szechwan
Taiwan		Taiwan
Xinjiang	Xinjiang Weiwu-er Zizhiqu	Sinkinag Uighur Autonomous Region
Xizang	Xizang Zizhiqu	Tibet Autonomous Region
Yunnan		Yunnan
Zhejiang		Chekiang

Appendix 3

DISTRIBUTION OF *IRIS* BY PROVINCE

Provinces are arranged across the top of the chart roughly from northeast to southwest with some attempt to correlate the distribution centers referred to in the text. The species, listed along the left margin, are arranged alphabetically with systematic groups. These systematic sequences are bearded irises, crested irises, beardless irises, subgenus *Nepalensis,* and genus *Pardanthopsis.*

	Heilongjiang	Jilin	Liaoning	Inner Mongolia	Hebei	Shandong	Shanxi	Henan	Jiangsu	Anhui	Zhejiang	Hubei	Fujian	Hunan	Jiangxi	Guangdong	Guangxi	Shaanxi	Ningxhia	Gansu	Sichuan	Yunnan	Tibet	Guizhou	Qinghai	Xinjiang	Cultivated	Taiwan
I. germanica																											•	
I. pallida																											•	
I. scariosa																										•		
I. bloudowii	•	•																								•		
I. curvifolia																										•		
I. flavissima	•																			•						•		
I. goniocarpa																	•				•	•	•	•	•			
I. kemaonensis																					•	•	•					
I. leptophylla																					•	•						
I. mandshurica	•	•	•																									
I. narcissiflora																					•							
I. pandurata																					•				•			
I. potaninii				•																	•	•	•		•			
I. sichuanensis																					•	•						
I. tigridia	•	•	•	•	•	•		•													•				•			
I. confusa																•					•	•				•		
I. formosana																												•
I. japonica									•	•	•	•	•	•	•	•	•	•	•		•	•	•	•			•	•
I. latistyla																						•						
I. milesii																					•	•	•					
I. proantha									•	•	•	•		•	•													
I. tectorum						•	•		•	•	•	•	•	•	•	•	•	•	•		•	•	•	•	•		•	•
I. wattii																					•	•						

APPENDIX 3. DISTRIBUTION OF *IRIS* BY PROVINCE

	Heilongjiang	Jilin	Liaoning	Inner Mongolia	Hebei	Shandong	Shanxi	Henan	Jiangsu	Anhui	Zhejiang	Hubei	Fujian	Hunan	Jiangxi	Guangdong	Guangxi	Shaanxi	Ningxhia	Gansu	Sichuan	Yunnan	Tibet	Guizhou	Qinghai	Xinjiang	Cultivated	Taiwan
I. subdichotoma (?)																						•						
I. henryi												•		•								•	•					
I. koreana			•																									
I. minutoaurea			•																									
I. rossii			•																									
I. speculatrix										•	•	•	•	•	•	•	•	•			•			•				
I. ruthenica	•	•	•	•	•	•	•	•	•		•							•	•	•	•	•	•			•		
I. uniflora	•	•	•	•																								
I. setosa		•																										
I. bulleyana																					•	•	•					
I. chrysographes																					•	•	•	•				
I. clarkei																						•	•					
I. delavayi																					•	•	•					
I. dykesii																												
I. forrestii																					•	•	•					
I. phragmitetorum																						•						
I. sanguinea	•	•	•	•					•																		•	
I. sibirica																											•	
I. typhifolia		•	•	•																								
I. wilsonii												•						•		•	•	•						
I. ensata	•	•	•	•		•					•																•	
I. laevigata	•	•	•																			•					•	
I. maackii	•		•																									
I. pseudacorus																											•	
I. versicolor																											•	
I. halophila																				•						•		
I. bungei			•		•										•					•	•							
I. cathayensis								•	•			•																
I. farreri																				•								
I. kobayashi			•																									
I. loczyi			•															•	•	•					•	•	•	
I. polysticta																		•	•	•	•				•			
I. quinghanica																									•			
I. songarica			•															•	•	•	•				•	•	•	
I. tenuifolia	•	•	•	•	•		•											•	•	•					•	•	•	
I. ventricosa	•	•	•	•	•																							
I. lactea	•	•	•	•	•	•	•	•	•	•	•	•			•			•	•	•	•	•	•		•	•	•	
I. anguifuga										•	•	•			•		•							•			•	
I. colletti																					•	•	•					
I. decora																					•	•	•					
P. dichotoma	•	•	•	•	•	•	•	•	•	•		•			•			•	•	•								

Appendix 4

CHINA HARDINESS ZONE MAP

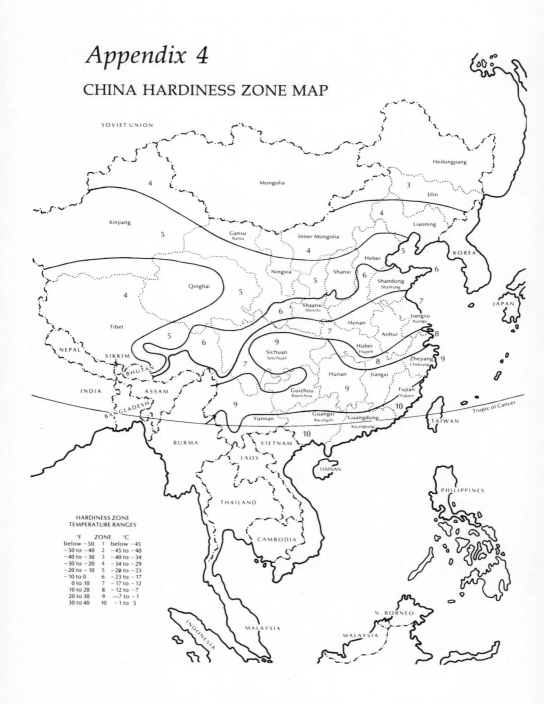

HARDINESS ZONE
TEMPERATURE RANGES

°F	ZONE	°C
below −50	1	below −45
−50 to −40	2	−45 to −40
−40 to −30	3	−40 to −34
−30 to −20	4	−34 to −29
−20 to −10	5	−29 to −23
−10 to 0	6	−23 to −17
0 to 10	7	−17 to −12
10 to 20	8	−12 to −7
20 to 30	9	−7 to −1
30 to 40	10	−1 to 5

Appendix 5

U.S. HARDINESS ZONE MAP

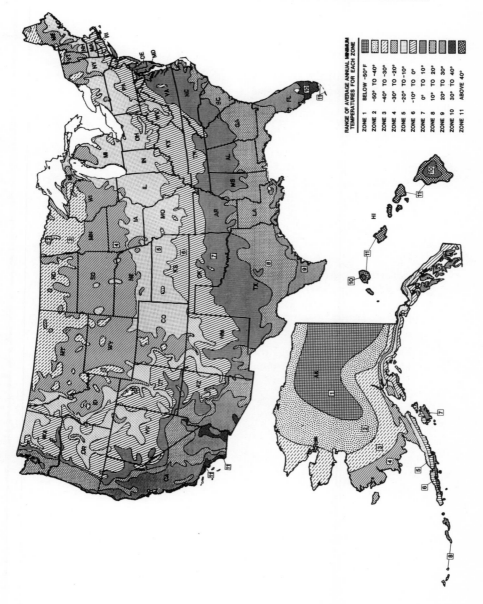

RANGE OF AVERAGE ANNUAL MINIMUM
TEMPERATURES FOR EACH ZONE

ZONE 1   BELOW –50° F
ZONE 2   –50° TO –40°
ZONE 3   –40° TO –30°
ZONE 4   –30° TO –20°
ZONE 5   –20° TO –10°
ZONE 6   –10° TO 0°
ZONE 7   0° TO 10°
ZONE 8   10° TO 20°
ZONE 9   20° TO 30°
ZONE 10   30° TO 40°
ZONE 11   ABOVE 40°

Appendix 6

NURSERY SOURCE LIST

The following nurseries sell various *Iris* species and cultivars as well as other general nursery stocks.

Adamgrove, Rte. 1, Box 246, Dept. I.C., California, MO 65018
    Species, Japanese and Siberian irises.
Busse Gardens, Rte. 2, Box 238, Cokato, MN 55321
    Species, Japanese, and Siberian cvs.
Cooper Gardens, 212 W. Co. Rd. C, Roseville, MN 55113
    Species, Japanese, and Siberian cvs.
Ensata Gardens, 9823 E. Michigan Ave., Galesburg, MI 49053
    Specializes in Japanese iris cvs. plus some Siberian cvs.
The Iris Pond, 7311 Churchill Rd., McLean, VA 22101
    Specializes in several types of irises including Japanese and
    Siberian cvs. Price list $1.
Laurie's Gardens, 41886 McKenzie Hwy., Springfield, OR 97478
    The largest selection of species, plus Japanese and Siberian cvs.
Redbud Lane Iris Gardens, Rte. 1, Box 141, Kansas, IL 61933
    Species irises.
We-Du Nurseries, Rte. 5, Box 724, Marion, N.C. 28752
    Uncommon species irises.

Appendix 7

CONVERSION TABLE—LENGTH

centimeter = 0.3937 inch   inch = 2.5400 centimeter
meter = 3.2808 feet   foot = 0.3048 meter
meter = 1.0936 yards   yard = 0.9144 meter
kilometer = 0.6214 mile   mile = 1.6093 kilometer

in	cm	ft	m
¼	0.6	.25	.07
½	1.3	.50	.15
¾	2.0	.75	.23
1	2.5	1.0	.30
1½	3.8	1.5	.45
2	5.0	2	.61
2½	6.4	3	.91
3	7.6	4	1.22
4	10.1	5	1.52
5	12.7	6	1.83
6	15.2	10	3.0
7	17.7		
8	20.3		
9	22.8		
10	25.4		
12	30.5		
15	38.1		
20	50.8		
24	61.0		
25	63.5		
30	76.2		
35	88.9		
36	91.4		
40	101.6		

Glossary

Part II, from the *Flora Reipublicae Popularis Sinicae,* contains some technical terms that may be unfamiliar to some readers in the context of iris. Various specific iris terms and general scientific words that appear in the text are included here.

Acuminate—Tapering to a point.
Acute—Sharply pointed.
Apex—The pointed end.
Apiculate—Ending abruptly in a short point.
Aril—An outgrowth, appendage, or covering of the seed. In *Iris* these are usually white or cream colored and restricted to certain species and groups within the genus. Function unknown.
Arillate—Bearing an aril.
Auricle—An earlike projection at the base of a petal or leaf.
Bract—A modified leaf subtending a flower or inflorescence.
Caudate—A tail-like part or having a tail.
Cilia—A small hairlike projection from an individual cell. Singular—cilium.
Claw—The narrowed clawlike base of the standard of the iris flower, although "haft" usually describes this part of both standard and fall (see Haft).
Coriaceous—Leathery.
Crenate—Having a notched or scalloped margin.
Crest 1—In *Iris* the usually fringelike ridge in the center of the fall of the flower of certain species (subgenus *Crossiris*).
   2—the terminal portions of the style arms. These are often distinctively shaped for certain species.
Cultivar—Any cultivated variety in horticulture. Usually a form or variety vegetatively propagated and given a non-Latinized cultivar name.
Cuneate—Describing the acute wedge-shaped angle at the base of the leaf or petal.
Cuneiform—Wedge shaped.
Deltoid—Triangular.

Dichotomous—Divided into two (usually equal or subequal) parts.

Ensiform—Having sharp edges and tapering to a point; sword or dagger shaped.

Endocarp—The innermost layer of the fruit or capsule (see Epicarp).

Epicarp—Exocarp; the outermost layer of the fruit or capsule.

Falcate—Sickle shaped or curved like a sickle.

Filament—The stalk of the stamen that bears an anther at its apex.

Filiform—Threadlike.

Fimbriate—Fringed; having a margin of fringe or fine hairs.

Glabrous—Smooth, hairless, usually describing a surface free of all projections.

Glaucous—Having a pale yellow-green or blue-green color; or covered in a pale gray or white waxy powder that can easily be wiped off.

Haft—The narrow base of the fall of the iris flower (see Claw).

Lanceolate—Lance shape; tapered at both ends and widest toward the basal portion.

Linear—Long narrow shape with edges parallel to each other.

Loculicidal—The splitting of a fruit or seed capsule along the edge of each locule or chamber, usually coinciding with the three prominent ridges.

Membranous—Thin, transparent, pliable.

Mucronate—A sharp abrupt terminal point.

Node—The point on a stem from which a leaf (or bud) arises.

Oblanceolate—A reversed lance shape; tapered at both ends and widest in the distal (outer) portion (see Lanceolate).

Obovate—A reversed egg shape; oval with the broadest portion at the distal end.

Obtuse—Blunt, dull; usually refers to the end of a leaf or petal.

Pandurate—A shape that is broad at the base, narrow in the middle, and broad at the end; violin shaped.

Pedicel—The stalk of an individual flower (see Peduncle).

Peduncle—The flower stem or main stalk of an inflorescence. Individual flowers are attached to the peduncle by their own pedicels.

Perianth—The outer parts of a flower consisting of calyx and corolla. In *Iris* the falls and standards comprise the perianth.

Pericarp—The wall of the fruit or seed capsule. In fleshy fruits it is easy to distinguish three layers: the outer epicarp, the middle usually fleshy mesocarp, and the inner endocarp. Iris fruits (seed pods) are usually dry and leathery, making these distinctions difficult.

Pubescent—Hairy, but usually referring to fine, short hairs.

Retuse—The apex being rounded or obtuse with a slight notch or indentation.

Scree—Technically, a rock or gravel slide at the base of a cliff; in horticulture, scree refers to a specially prepared bed of rocks and stone topped by a thinner layer of sand, gravel, soil, or humus, as appropriate. These beds are usually raised and provide extreme drainage.

Spatulate—Spoon shaped; having a broad, rounded end and tapering to a narrow base at the point of attachment.

Stoloniferous—Bearing creeping, above-ground, usually horizontal stems. These stolons rarely bear leaves in *Iris*.

Style arm—The portion of the female reproductive structure of a flower that connects the pollen-receiving stigma with the ovary. In *Iris* the style is divided into three style arms (sometimes called branches) which are usually flattened and petaloid. The style arm tips, beyond the stigma, are called the crests and are sometimes enlarged into distinctive shapes.

Transverse—Crosswise or at right angles to the main axis.

Trichome—Any outgrowth from an epidermal cell. In *Iris* these are usually hairlike and used in taxonomy and identification.

Type species—The named species that forms the basis for a genus. In *Iris* the type species is *I. germanica*.

Type specimen—The named specimen that forms the basis for a species. Each species has its own named type specimen usually located in a museum or herbarium.

Valve—A segment of a seed pod after the pod has ripened and split.

Bibliography

GENERAL AND SYSTEMATICS

Dykes, W. R. 1913. *The Genus Iris.* Cambridge: Cambridge Univ. Press.

How, F. C., ed. 1984. *A Dictionary of the Families and Genera of Chinese Seed Plants.* 2nd ed. Beijing: Science Press.

Kohlein, F. 1987. *Iris.* Portland, OR: Timber Press.

Lancaster, R. 1989. *Travels in China—A Plantsman's Paradise.* Woodbridge, Suffolk: Antique Collector's Club.

Marchant, A. and B. Mathew, eds. 1974. *An Alphabetical Table and Cultivation Guide to the Species of the Genus Iris.* London: British Iris Society.

Mathew, B. 1983. Misc. Notes on Iris Species. In *The Iris Yearbook. 1983.* 92–96. London: British Iris Society.

_____ . 1989. *The Iris.* rev. ed. London: B. T. Batsford.

_____ . 1990. A Note on the Nomenclature of Iris Kemaonensis. *Kew Magazine* 7(1):13–14.

Rodionenko, G. I. 1984. *The Genus Iris L. (Questions of Morphology, Biology, Evolution and Systematics).* London: British Iris Society.

Stevens, J. 1952. *The Iris and its Culture.* Melbourne, Aust.: Lothian Pub. Co.

Walters, S. M., A. Brady, C. D. Brickell et al., eds. 1986. *The European Garden Flora,* vol. I. Cambridge: Cambridge Univ. Press.

Warburton, B. and M. Hamblen, eds. 1978. *The World of Iris.* Wichita, KS: American Iris Society.

FLORAS

Cowan, J. M. 1952. *The Journeys and Plant Introductions of George Forrest V. M. H.* London: Oxford Univ. Press.

Fang, W. P. 1942–46. *Icones Plantarum Omeiensium.* Beijing: Science Press.

Forbes, F. B. and W. H. Hemsley. 1903–1905. *An Enumeration of all*

BIBLIOGRAPHY

the plants known from China Proper, Formosa, Hainan, Corea, the Luchu Archipelago and the Island of Hongkong together with their Distribution and Synonomy. vol. 3. Reprint, 1980. Koenigstein,W. Germany: O. Koeltz Sci. Publ.

Fu, H. C. et al., eds. 1985. Flora Intermongolica, Tomus 8. Huhehaot'e, Inner Mongolia: Inn. Mong. People's Press.

Grey-Wilson, C. 1988. Journey to the Jade Dragon Snow Mountain, Yunnan. Parts 1–4. Quarterly Bull. of the Alpine Gard. Soc. 56(1) no. 231:15–34; 56(2) no. 232:115–130; 56(3) no. 233: 221–242; 56(4) no. 234:289–306.

Hara, H. 1966. The Flora of the Eastern Himalaya. Tokyo, Japan: Univ. of Tokyo Press.

Hensley, W. B. (with H. H. Pearson). 1902. The Flora of Tibet or High Asia. Journ. Linn. Soc. Bot. 35:124–265.

How, F. C. 1956. Flora of Canton. Beijing: Science Press.

Iconographia Cormophytorum Sinicorum, Tomus 5, 2nd ed. 1987. Beijing: Science Press.

Jiangsu Inst. of Bot., eds. 1977. Flora of Jiangsu. Nanjing: Jiangsu Inst. of Bot.

Kitagawa, M. 1979. Neo-Lineamenta Flora Manshurica. Vaduz, Lichtenstein: Cramer.

Komarov, V. I. 1960. Flora of the USSR Eng. ed. vol. 4, Iris. Jerusalem: Israel Proj. for Sci. Transl.

Li, H. L. et al, eds. 1975–79. Flora of Taiwan. Taipei: Epoch.

Nair, N.C. 1977. Flora of Bashahor Himalayas, Madras. Hissar, Haryana: Int. Biosci. Publ.

Nakai, T., M. Honda, Y. Satake, and M. Kitagawa. 1936. Index Florae Jeholensis, Sect. IV (4). Tokyo: Rept. of 1st Sci. Exp. to Manchukuo.

Nakao S. and K. Nishioka. 1984. Flowers of Bhutan. Tokyo: Asahi Shimbun Pub.

Nasir, E. and S. I. Ali, eds. 1972. Flora of W. Pakistan. Karachi: Dept. of Bot., Univ. of Karachi.

Ohwi, J. 1984. Flora of Japan (in English). Washington, D.C.: Smithsonian Press.

Polunin, O. and A. Stainton. 1984. Flowers of the Himalaya. Oxford: Oxford Univ. Press.

Steward, A. N. 1958. Manual of Vascular Plants of the Lower Yangtze Valley, China. Corvallis: Ore. St. Coll.

Waddick, J. W. 1989. China Iris Project—Post Trip Report. SIGNA. Species Iris Group of North America. 43:1546–1558.

_____ . 1990. Collecting Wild Iris in China. Bull. Amer. Iris Soc. 71(1):63–79.

Wang, C. W. 1961. *Forests of China*. Boston: Harvard Univ. Press.

Wu, C. I., ed. 1977–79. *Flora Yunnanica*. Beijing: Science Press.

Wu, C. Y., ed. 1987. *Flora Xizangaica*. Beijing: Science Press.

Yen, C. 1989. *Native Species of Iris to Sichuan Province*. Photocopy.

Zhao, Y. T. 1980. Some Notes on the Genus Iris of China. *Acta Phyto. Sinica* 18(1):53–62.

_____. 1982. The Geographical Distribution of *Iris* in China. *The Iris Yearbook, 1982*. 47–51. London: British Iris Society.

_____. 1985. *Flora Reipulicae Popularis Sinicae*, Tomus 16(1) Iridaceae. Beijing: Science Press.

CULTIVATION

British Iris Society. 1979. *The Cultivation of Irises. Part I: Bearded Irises*. London: British Iris Society.

Cassady, G. E. and S. Linnegar. 1982. *Growing Irises*. London: Croom Helm.

Grosvenor, G. 1984. *Growing Irises*. Kenthurst, Australia: Kangaroo Press.

Osborn, E. G. 1979. *The Cultivation of Irises. Part II: Beardless Irises*. London: British Iris Society.

Waddick, J. W. 1990. Chinese Irises; the Rare, the New and the Lovely. Pacific Horticulture 31(2):25–29.

CHROMOSOMES

Chimphamba, B. B. 1973. Cytogenetic Studies in the Genus Iris: Subsection *Evansia*, Benth. *Cytologia* 38:501–514.

Doronkin, V. M. and A. A. Krasnikov. 1984. Cytotaxonomic Studies in some Siberian Species of *Iris* (Iridicaeae). *Bot. Zurn. SSSR*. 65 (5):683–685.

Longley, A. E. 1928. Chromosomes in Iris Species. *Bull. Amer. Iris Soc.* 29:43–55.

Mao, Q. and X. J. Xue. 1986. Chromosome Numbers of Thirteen Iridaceous Species from Zhejiang Province. *Acta. Agric. Univ. Zhejiang. Prov.* 12:99–101.

Sharma, A. K. 1970. Annual Report 1967–1968. *Res. Bull. Univ. Calcutta (Cytogenetics Lab.)* 2:1–50.

Simonet, Marc. 1928. Le Nombre des Chromosomes dans le genre *Iris. Compt. Rend. Soc. Biol.* 99(30):1314–1316.

_____. 1932. Recherches Cytologiques et Genetique chez les *Iris. Bull. Biol. de la France et de le Belgique* 105:255–444.

_____. 1934. Nouvelles recherches Cytologiques et Genetiques

BIBLIOGRAPHY

chez les *Iris. Ann. Sci. Nat. Bot Ser. 10e* 16:229–383.
_____ . 1952 Nouveaux denoubrements Chromosomiques chez les *Iris. Compt. Rend. Acad. Aci. (Paris)* 232:875–878.
Zakharyeva, O. I. and L. M. Makushenko. 1969. Chromosome Numbers of Monocotyledons Belonging to the Familes Liliaceae, Iridaceae, Amaryllidaceae, Araceae. *Bot. Zurn.* 54:1213–1227.
Zhao, Y. T. 1986. Karyotype Studies of 3 species of Genus *Iris* in China. *Journ. N.E. Norm. Univ.* 2(2):71–78.

SPECIFIC ACCOUNTS

Ansley, G. and the Earl of Rosse. 1987. Iris Speculatrix. *SIGNA.* Species Iris Study Group of the Amer. Iris Soc. 38:1353–1354.
Berlin, E. 1989. A New Iris for Very Cold Climates. *The Siberian Iris* 6(9):12–15.
Grey-Wilson, C. 1971. *The Genus Iris—Subsection Sibiricae.* London: British Iris Society.
Horinaka, Akira. 1990. *The Pictorial Book of Iris laevigata.* Ohuna, Japan: ABOCSHA Co., Ltd.
McEwen, C. 1981. *Siberian Irises.* Hayward: Soc. for Siberian Irises.
_____ . 1990. *The Japanese Iris.* Hannover: Brandeis University Press by University Press of New England.
Noltie, H. 1990. *141. Iris Dolichosiphon,* Iridaceae. *Kew Magazine* 7(1):9–13.
Qi, Y. B. and Y. T. Zhao. 1987. Studies on the Pollen Morphology of the genus *Iris* in China. *Acta. Phyto. Sinica.* 25(6):430–436.
Zhao, Y. T. 1982. New Taxa of *Iris* L. from China. *Acta. Phyto. Sinica.* 20(1):99–100.

Index

An asterisk * following a page number indicates a line drawing.